Date Due

JAN 2 1954			
JAN 2 1954			
JAN 2 2 1954			
JAN 2 5 1954			
JAN 2 5 1954			
JUL 22			
AUG 2 4 1987			

Reduce and Enjoy It
COOKBOOK

REDUCE
& ENJOY IT
COOKBOOK

by
ELAINE L. ROSS

PREFACE BY
IRVING H. BECKWITH, M.D.

DRAWINGS BY
PAUL CALLÉ

HARPER & BROTHERS PUBLISHERS
NEW YORK

Library of Congress catalog card number: 53-7743

613

Contents

20117

Preface

In a world where people in many countries are suffering from malnutrition, if not actually starving, the great problem in our country is overeating. Keeping one's weight down usually concerns nearly everyone at some point in his life, and to many it requires continual effort.

It is interesting to read through a very typical account of this constant struggle with overweight, and to study Mrs. Ross's answer to such a great and prevalent medical problem. Not being satisfied with routine medical advice, the author, in a clear, scientific and intelligent manner, has worked out a large series of appetizing menus which are certain to encourage and challenge the would-be dieter to tackle the job with more anticipation than dread.

By being clear and sound, by avoiding the monotony of the usual prescribed reducing diet, and by creating interesting and varied meals, she has set up a regime that will be pleasant to adhere to for as long a period of time as is necessary to effect the required weight reduction. At the same time, the dieter is learning and becoming accustomed to a way of eating that will maintain a proper weight for good health.

Preface

Besides being a boon to the many people who have to watch their weight, this book by Mrs. Ross can be of tremendous help to busy doctors who would like to prescribe more interesting reducing diets but do not have the time.

IRVING H. BECKWITH, M.D.

White Plains, New York

Reduce and Enjoy It
COOKBOOK

1. Right in the Thick of It

"ISN'T she a healthy specimen?"

I can still hear my mother's voice tinged with pride in the accomplishment of having stuffed me so well that at the age of seven I weighed ninety-nine pounds. Life was just a bowl of whipped cream until, when I was ten, my mother's disheartening shopping expeditions with me ended up in the girdle department. The healthy specimen couldn't fit into any of the girls' department's offerings, and really it was a bit too young to start with misses' dresses. Finding that what a girdle restrained in one spot by the inexorable laws of nature and physics just had to pop out in another, the only recourse seemed to be diet, or exercise, or both.

Then and there started a horrible succession of gym classes, reducing salons and the introduction of every new diet fad. I was steamed in the cabinet bath, assaulted by fire hoses, pummeled by any number of healthy, hearty young Swedish women. Of course, I never confessed that I found consolation in a chocolate soda after each visit to the torture chamber. Nobody could understand why twenty treatments found me eight pounds heavier.

At that time, the first of the eighteen-day diets was publicized. With that began several weeks of thick lamb chops, steak, plain lettuce (how horrible!), tomatoes and grapefruit. I still abhor grapefruit. The eighteen days resulted in a loss of eight to nine pounds. The following two weeks showed a gain of at least ten.

Interspersed with these "miracle diets" were the "sensible diets" prescribed by a physician. "Just cut out starches, fats and sweets. Eat all the meat you want, vegetables, fruit and Jello." But what sense could these diets make to a teen-ager brought up in a home in which great stress was placed on the richness and delectability of the cooking? In particular, what sense could they make when that teen-ager had learned to appreciate and enjoy a fine table? I adhered to the diet for a month, or perhaps two. I lost from ten to twenty pounds. In time, though, the craving for all the forbidden foods was just too much, and the first piece of candy was the beginning of each downfall. A month or so later, I began letting out the notches in the belt again.

Hopefully, each year or so, I submitted to a metabolism test, only to find that while I was consistently on the borderline of being hypothyroid, I was still in the normal category. Even then, I was given a small dosage of thyroid. That didn't help, either.

During all this time my mother's friends would talk about "baby fat," saying that when I was seventeen or eighteen I would lose it all. The hoped-for alchemy never took place. My twentieth birthday saw me almost five feet nine in my stocking feet, and a perfect size twenty. A year later, at the time of my marriage, I was a sixteen for an all-too-short time.

Right in the Thick of It

Six months after that it was an eighteen and, in no time at all, back to a twenty. I think now that the dressmakers must have vied for my patronage during those and the preceding years, when my average fluctuation was between ten and twenty pounds. From the time I was twenty-two, I settled into a more or less permanently comfortable size twenty.

This was interrupted briefly by a doctor who gave me a prescribed diet of high protein content, amplified by lettuce, tomatoes and citrus fruits. There was one near-starvation day weekly and, to compensate, a small piece of apple pie every Sunday. The weekly weighing-in at his office frightened me sufficiently to maintain the diet while I was under his surveillance. At the end of six months I was again wearing a size sixteen. I don't have to tell you what the size tag on the dress was three months later.

To complicate matters, the twenty-one-year-old who, at the time of her marriage, was one of those proverbial novices who couldn't boil water became in short order a better than average cook. I liked cooking and I could do it well. I was in my glory trying a new recipe which called for a half pound of butter and a pint of heavy cream. I was still more in my glory eating amply of the successful result.

During all this time I was a model of apparent unconcern when I brought home a new dress and my husband commented, "It would look fine if you lost ten or fifteen pounds." Each time a well-meaning friend (and I use the word advisedly) made some suggestion about losing weight, I parried by saying that I felt just fine. I never confessed the deep hurt which this implied criticism caused. Nor did I pay any heed when the doctor advised that all this extra weight was

3

medically unwise. "That," I thought, "I shall worry about when I'm older." Though all the criticism and suggestion hurt, because they were so completely justified, they just didn't hurt enough to warrant my going back to exhausting overdoses of physical punishment or to giving up the sensual pleasure of the gourmand's table.

Covertly, from time to time, I had studied the ads that featured "Before" and "After" results. A careful analysis of the two pictures invariably showed the former full face, standing badly, in a light-colored dress, with flat-heeled shoes and a generally unkempt appearance. The "After" portrait was done either three-quarter or side view, and showed the lady well groomed in a dark dress and higher heels. "She," I thought to myself, "wouldn't have looked half so bad in the first place had the photographer and the wardrobe mistress used equal skill on both occasions."

Then there were the reducing machines which I investigated briefly. When I checked their merit with a doctor he answered me, "There's only one machine that's of any value in reducing, and that's a scale."

Last year, as a fifteenth anniversary "second honeymoon," my husband and I spent two months in Europe. The fame of the French cuisine is well deserved. I came home with all kinds of culinary ideas which I promptly put into effect. The home cooking was better than ever and so was my size. I also returned home with a tremendous desire to revisit Europe in short order and at greater length. My husband thought he'd found my Achilles' heel (he had!) when he bribed me with the promise of another trip in a few years if I lost fifteen pounds.

I had heard talk among my friends of calorie diets. True, I had paid scant attention to any such distasteful discussion. Now, I mused, it might be possible to plan a diet which could incorporate my French-found ideas to a degree, and which wouldn't contain one grapefruit section. My first step was to invest in a pocket-sized calorie chart. A casual study of it revealed that many of the foods that I enjoyed were not so high in caloric content as I would have guessed; for instance, ice cream, bacon, cream cheese, to mention a few. Conversely, some were shockingly high. The nutritive value of an avocado floored me.

I chose a thousand calories a day as my allotment. I'd heard some of the women speaking of thousand-calorie diets. Next, I went to a local distributor of health and diet foods and bought a selection of low-caloric food substitutes. I tried several jams, a chocolate sauce, saccharin and sucaryl, a diet mayonnaise made without mineral oil, cookies, bread stuffs and so forth. Most I found unpalatable, but some I made use of in my diet. I still eat the bread sticks, the zwieback-like rusks, and use the chocolate sauce, saccharin and mayonnaise. This last, I've discovered, is fine, tempered with a few drops of lemon juice.

I then set about studying my favorite recipes from a caloric angle. Some I realized did not seem too high. With others, I tried cutting down on the butter, substituting skimmed milk for heavy cream in sauces, but using herbs and wine to enhance the flavor. I did not try to eliminate the use of fattening ingredients, but rather limited the quantity used. The results were certainly good. The dishes did not perhaps taste so rich, but I learned that a Chicken-in-Wine-à-la-Calories can be a tasteful and satisfying dish. I selected the foods which I liked and ignored those of which I was not fond. In general, when planning a menu, I combined a low-calorie main dish with rice or potatoes or a richer dessert, and vice versa. I did not go to the ridiculous or unnecessary extreme of weighing or measuring my portions of food. I am sure that I erred often, but the mistakes could not have been too serious, as was proved by the results. Another difficulty is that the calorie guides do not list all foods. Many times I ate an unknown quantity. Again, the results proved that my estimate had been fairly accurate. Ofttimes I had a craving between meals for something sweet. I didn't hazard a Hershey bar, but fruit Life Savers or gum drops aren't bad at all.

It must be kept in mind that a calorie chart can only list the average value of many foods. It is possible to scramble an egg with one-half teaspoon or with one tablespoon of butter; one-half cup of gravy can be ninety percent or five percent fat. It is better, when possible, to add up the component caloric parts rather than to accept the average quoted. I have included, though, some of these averages in my caloric table. When dining out, use these figures. When you're at home, you know what goes into the preparation of the food.

During the first two weeks of the diet I found that the only difficult time of day was about four in the afternoon. I had decided to have a small breakfast and lunch and to concentrate the bulk of my caloric allotment on dinner, when the children and my husband were home. By midafternoon, though, I was hungry enough, after a normally active housewife's day, to eat anything just to stop that persistent gnawing. A cup of coffee, I discovered, is a godsend until dinner.

7

The distribution of calories throughout the day is, of course, largely dependent on individual activity and preference. I allowed three hundred or three hundred and fifty for breakfast and lunch combined, hoarding my six hundred and fifty or seven hundred for the evening meal. Caloric intake is based on the size of the individual, amount of weight to be lost, length of time for the diet and daily activity. This figure should be suggested by the family physician.

The first sixteen days of "eating differently" yielded a loss of nine pounds. I can hardly call it dieting in the same fashion as the previous horrors I had endured. I enjoyed eating. I had no craving for any particular food, because if I had, I included it, though perhaps in a small amount, in that day's menu. I was elated by this practically painless dieting and completely amazed by its rapid success.

"I'd better check this quickly with the doctor," I thought, "to make sure that I haven't devised some harmful regime." It just seemed too good to be true. The doctor's findings and comments on my diet were all encouraging. He approved the thousand-calorie daily intake. My physical condition was good and he didn't see why it shouldn't stay that way. He did suggest that I take one multiple-vitamin capsule daily.

After two months I had lost eighteen pounds. During the third month I started wearing a size sixteen again. My husband's bribe was no longer the impetus to maintain the diet. When I started wearing younger, more extreme styles, that was more than enough reward. By the end of the fifth month I had dropped thirty-two pounds and wore a size fourteen. At least a dozen times I was reintroduced to people I had known for many years but hadn't seen in the last six months. It may

have been an embarrassing experience for them, but it was a most gratifying one for my ego. At the end of the sixth month I had lost forty pounds and occasionally could buy a size twelve dress.

It's a well-known saying that imitation is the most sincere form of flattery. So many people started to question me as to what I ate and what I eliminated from my diet that I began to feel a bit like a public exhibit. I did notice, though, that a number of them were apparently sufficiently impressed by my accomplishment to follow my example. I was surprised at first when even some of the men who had traded in a "football physique" for a "bay window" started asking just as many questions as had their wives. Since my diet was such a flexible one, it was relatively much easier for them to follow than any prescribed routine. Lunch at a drugstore counter or in an office was not the problem that it had been on a diet of specific menus. It tickled me to hear enthusiastic reports of their progress.

At that point the doctor advised me not to lose any more weight. I was tempted to have a recording made of his voice as he said it. No one had ever said that to me before. A metabolism test indicated that a diet for me to maintain proper weight should include fifteen to sixteen hundred calories.

Fourteen months have passed since that time. I weigh in every morning. If I find that I've lost a pound and have it to gain back, I make a batch of griddlecakes and eat them with a clear conscience. If I've gained a pound, I cut down the caloric intake for a day or two.

I feel fairly safe now in writing this book. I don't think that a year from now I'll be rereading it dressed in my latest

Stylish Stout. It really wasn't too hard to get this way. I still enjoy cooking. I still enjoy eating. I buy every new cookbook that is published. My vanity, though, won't let me go back up—if the vanity isn't omnipresent, and I should be tempted, I quickly glance at the day's sailings for Europe.

2. And This Is How It Worked

As I have said before, the menus I planned were based on my personal food preferences. The allotment of calories for the three meals was again dependent on my needs and desires. The menus which I present here are not inflexible and should serve only as a guide and possible suggestion for your own imaginative planning. You will notice that there are fairly few broiled foods in contrast to most diets. The reason for this is that it is my belief that most foods that are not fatty of themselves are dry and unpalatable unless broiled with liberal amounts of butter or fat. On the other hand, it is possible to braise or pot a meat or poultry using a minimum of fat to brown it. Then, by adding water or stock to finish the cooking, you can serve a dish which is both juicy and toothsome.

I had never had a large appetite at breakfast time, so that meal was easy to plan. Merely by cutting down the amount of juice or fruit, and substituting skimmed milk and saccharin for the cream and sugar in my coffee, I arrived at a breakfast that satisfied me and certainly pared down the caloric intake. I submit only three sample breakfasts. They were the ones I adhered to during the diet. By consulting your calorie chart, you can make any substitutions you prefer. Should you need more sustenance at breakfast, substitute a piece of toast with the merest suggestion of butter. (Try spreading the bread with butter and then setting it under the broiler. A smaller amount of butter seems to go further and the taste is delicious this way.) For breakfast, I discovered a zwieback-like diet rusk, made of artichoke flour; only eight calories each, and very good! Don't forget, though, if you do add to this meal to subtract the additional breakfast calories from another meal.

For lunch I often ate sandwiches. By cutting the bread a little thinner and by selecting the less fattening fillings among those I enjoyed, I found that it was feasible to include sandwiches often on the diet. This, of course, was where I made good use of my low-calorie mayonnaise. I don't like dry sandwiches and didn't have to eat them that way at home. Naturally, when I was lunching at a restaurant, I had to take the bread as it came and asked for sandwiches without butter or mayonnaise. More often, though, at a restaurant I ordered an egg dish for lunch. You will notice among the luncheon menus a preponderance of egg, fish or cheese dishes. In general, their caloric value is lower than that of meat.

I do not include here any allowance for alcoholic beverage. I found that I preferred to eat my calories rather than to drink them. However, there is no necessity to eliminate them. Just don't forget to subtract the necessary calories from dinner. When I did have a drink, it was either straight or with soda. The caloric content of cocktails and mixed drinks was too astronomical to permit their inclusion.

There were certain foods which I did cut out. Those which concentrated a high number of calories in small bulk I felt should be left out. I found so many others that were more satiating without having more food value.

While I prepared many dishes with sauces and gravies, I did not lavish them on my own servings. I took enough to enjoy the dish thoroughly but not more.

I tried, in planning the evening meal, to be practical. I ate things that my family, too, would enjoy. Of course I had my portion of vegetables without butter, took less gravy and left most of the whipped cream toppings off my desserts, in general. Still, this type of planning eliminated special "diet" cooking.

In experimenting with recipes, I found that sometimes it was feasible to use substitutes to lower the caloric value, such as saccharin or a commercial diet chocolate sauce or mayonnaise. I have only included those recipes in which the result with the substitute ingredient was as palatable as the original. If it wasn't, I used the original ingredient called for, though less of it.

While this diet does include certain quantities of milk used in cooking, it does not include enough for a growing child. Should you be planning a diet for a teen-ager, I suggest adding two glasses of skimmed milk. To compensate for this, either reduce the portion of starchy vegetable at dinnertime, or substitute another of lower caloric content. Also simplify the dessert by either eliminating the garnish or cutting down the size of the portion.

As you glance through the menus, particularly the dinner ones, you will notice a preponderance of "fancy" dishes and relatively few prosaic ones. I feel that the broiled chops and steak are known to everyone. By all means use them, when you will. I do want to show, however, that diet cooking can also be streamlined party cooking; and that party cooking can be easy cooking.

This type of flexible diet, as opposed to the more rigidly prescribed doctor's diet, permitted me to accept any dinner or party invitations. I could always find enough to eat, and even saved some of my calories for dessert. At one party my dinner partner was a physician. He laughed at me as he noticed that I took a small portion of a rich dessert and simultaneously put saccharin in my coffee. He said that women who did such contradictory things amused him. I explained that the substitution of saccharin for sugar in my four cups of coffee during the day permitted me to have that small sampling of dessert. I'd enjoyed the dessert and the coffee could still be sweet. He remarked that he'd never thought of a diet from that angle. How all too true! I think that were doctors to try to live for any length of time on the monotonously repetitive diets they prescribe, they would have no more will power than their patients.

To all these doctors then, and to their long-suffering patients, may I submit a few of my ideas.

15

3. An Ounce of Prevention

BEFORE I get to the menus, though, a word about my daughter. She's just turned fifteen. Everyone says that she looks just like me. Certainly she takes after me—she loves to eat! Not long ago, we began to notice the shape of things to come. It wasn't good. While there might be a question as to whether her features resembled mine, there was no doubt that she was heading straight for the same size twenty. Let me add that she was far from alone with her problem. About half her contemporaries of both sexes are constantly struggling to hold that line. Unfortunately, they alternately gorge themselves on all the lunchroom goodies—the ice-cream sandwiches, potato chips, baked beans and candy bars, or starve on an orange for lunch. Naturally, the results are not productive. Very soon they're right back bemoaning their fate, and doing nothing else about it.

Before matters got too far out of hand with Jill, we consulted our physician to determine what her weight loss should be, and how many calories her diet should permit. He advised a loss of twenty pounds (though she's aiming for twenty-five

to give herself a little leeway) and a daily diet of a thousand calories.

She's just finishing her sixth week, and has lost seventeen pounds. There's a definite physical change, of course, but almost more important is the striking personality metamorphosis. She's so pleased with her accomplishment, and so much more self-confident now, that she just glows with happiness. Both her friends and mine have remarked that she seems a different girl.

Let me caution all dieters, young and old, that the rate of loss is not a constant one. There will be a marked loss at first, followed by a period of leveling off. A week or ten days may go by after the initial weight reduction, and show only a difference of a half pound or a pound. By all means, don't get discouraged and give up. It is particularly important that your youngster should be warned to anticipate this.

In making up the menus for Jill, there were several considerations that had not entered into planning my meals. The doctor advised including a minimum of two six-ounce glasses of skimmed milk daily. This necessitated subtracting those calories elsewhere. She prefers one glass midafternoon, since lunch period at school is at eleven-fifteen, and the afternoon milk tides her over until dinnertime. The second consideration was school lunches, which meant sandwiches for the most part. (A new low-starch brown bread has very recently been put on the market. The slices are substantial, and the taste is very palatable.) It is possible to include salads in paper containers, but my experience was that she didn't want to be different from her schoolmates. That would have made an issue of her diet, and adolescents are notably sensitive. Unfortunately, most school cafeterias find that their budgets limit them to the more economical starchy foods; therefore, lunches had to be sent from home.

To substitute for the gum and candies, Jill uses a sugarless gum and some fruit-flavored candies at one calorie each. Not a Hershey bar, to be sure, but she seems satisfied. She also discovered sugarless carbonated drinks—root beer, raspberry soda and so forth, so that she need not look longingly while the crowd is sipping Cokes. Of course, her diet is supplemented with the same multiple-vitamin capsule that I have been taking.

As with the adult menus, these are equally flexible. Jill doesn't require much food in the morning. Then, too, her lunch period is so early. Consequently, the breakfast is very light. However, as I have said before, the proportions may be juggled to suit the child. According to the doctor, it makes no difference when the food is eaten, as long as the nutritive value, balance of foods and caloric content is correct.

In planning menus 28 through 31, I have tried to incorporate foods that have a general appeal to youngsters. Their palates may not be so receptive to the wine and herb school of cooking. Let me repeat that these are only suggested menus to start you off on a train of ideas.

After this period of time has elapsed, and particularly after an initial resistance to any form of diet, Jill admits that it really hasn't been hard at all. I trust that that thought will prevent her from following her mother's path up and down the scale, with all its attendant misery. I hope that her "ounce of prevention" has truly effected the cure.

Perhaps, like all parents, I want things better for my child. I believe that in this one small respect I have succeeded.

BREAKFAST MENUS

4. Breakfast Menus

For Breakfast I Ate Either—

BREAKFAST 1—45 calories
$\frac{1}{4}$ medium cantaloupe
2 diet zwieback
1 cup coffee
Saccharin, 1 tablespoon skimmed milk

BREAKFAST 2—45 calories
$\frac{1}{8}$ medium honeydew
2 diet zwieback
1 cup coffee
Saccharin, 1 tablespoon skimmed milk

BREAKFAST 3—55 calories
$\frac{1}{4}$ cup orange juice
2 diet zwieback
1 cup coffee
Saccharin, 1 tablespoon skimmed milk

Jill's Breakfast Is Either—

BREAKFAST 1—50 calories
$\frac{1}{2}$ grapefruit
2 diet zwieback

BREAKFAST 2—45 calories
$\frac{2}{3}$ cup tomato juice
2 diet zwieback

LUNCH and DINNER MENUS and RECIPES FOR 31 DAYS

5. Lunch and Dinner Menus and Recipes for Thirty-one Days

MENU 1

LUNCHEON—235 calories
2 Hamburgers—180 calories
Pickled Beets—50 calories
Coffee with skimmed milk and saccharin—5 calories

Hamburgers

¼ *pound lean ground round steak*
1 *teaspoon mustard*
1 *teaspoon garlic salt*
salt

Mix meat with garlic salt and mustard. Preheat heavy iron frying pan. Sprinkle salt in pan. Panbroil hamburgers, turning once until they reach desired rareness.

Pickled Beets

½ *cup sliced cooked beets*
½ *teaspoon sugar*
2 *teaspoons vinegar*
1 *teaspoon beet juice*

Combine juice, vinegar and sugar. Pour over cooked beets. Allow to marinate for at least one hour.

27

DINNER—660 calories

Veal Scallopini in Wine—300 calories each portion
1 cup Cauliflower—35 calories
¾ cup Broad Noodles with Parmesan Cheese—125 calories
Glazed Strawberry Tart—195 calories each portion
Coffee with skimmed milk and saccharine—5 calories

Veal Scallopini in Wine (serves four)

3 tablespoons sherry
8 slices veal, approximately 4 inches by 3 inches by ¼ inch
3 tablespoons butter
1 clove garlic, minced
2 large mushrooms, chopped
1 teaspoon chili sauce
1 teaspoon meat concentrate
1½ tablespoons flour
1½ cups bouillon or stock
salt, black pepper, bay leaf

Have veal pounded into very thin slices. Brown meat in hot butter in heavy iron skillet. Pour hot sherry over meat. Remove veal. Add minced garlic and mushrooms. Cook one minute. Blend in chili sauce, meat concentrate and flour. Gradually add hot bouillon, stirring constantly until it boils. Put back veal. Season with salt and pepper. Add bay leaf. Cover and simmer for 25 minutes.

Cauliflower

Cook one medium head of cauliflower in boiling salted water about 25 minutes until tender. Garnish with chopped parsley.

Broad Noodles

Cook broad noodles in boiling, salted water until tender, about 10 minutes. Drain in a colander and rinse under cold water.

Sprinkle each portion with two tablespoons Parmesan cheese, freshly grated if possible.

Glazed Strawberry Tart (serves eight)
- ⅓ *cup vegetable shortening*
- 1 *cup cake flour*
- ⅓ *teaspoon salt*
- 2½ *tablespoons boiling water*
- 1 *teaspoon milk*
- 4 *cups strawberries*
- 1½ *tablespoons cornstarch*
- ⅓ *cup sugar*
- 1 *teaspoon lemon juice*

Crust—Pour boiling water and milk over shortening. Beat until creamy. Cool. Blend in flour and salt, stirring quickly and lightly. Shape into round, flat circle. Roll out between two pieces of waxed paper into circle a little larger than pie plate. Loosen paper on top and bottom of dough. Peel off top paper. Fit pastry into pan, pastry side down. Pull off other paper. Make fluted edge. Prick dough all over with fork. Bake at 450° for 15 minutes, or until light brown.

Filling—Wash, stem and dry berries. Reserve half of the nicest berries. Mash the other half. Add cornstarch, sugar and lemon juice to the mashed berries. Cook over moderate heat, stirring until thick and clear. Cool. Arrange whole berries in pie shell. Pour cooled glaze over all and chill.

MENU 2

LUNCHEON—220 calories

Fresh Salmon and Cucumber Salad—215 calories
Coffee with saccharin and skimmed milk—5 calories

Fresh Salmon and Cucumber Salad

salmon steak (4 inches by 2¼ inches by ½ inch)
3 *peppercorns*
1 *bayleaf*
1 *tablespoon vinegar*
salt, pepper
10 *medium slices cucumber*
3 *leaves lettuce*
1 *tablespoon diet mayonnaise*
1 *tablespoon chili sauce*
few drops lemon juice
1 *teaspoon chopped chives*

Poach salmon gently in 1 cup boiling water to which salt, peppercorns, bayleaf and vinegar have been added. Turn off heat after 10 minutes and allow salmon to cool in stock. Arrange salmon on lettuce. Surround with cucumber slices. Pour dressing of mayonnaise, chili sauce and lemon juice over all, and garnish with chives.

DINNER—715 calories

½ pound Boiled Beef with Horseradish
Sauce—430 calories
1 Bouillon Potato—45 calories
2 large Carrots—60 calories
Lemon Cream Pie—175 calories each portion
Coffee with saccharin and skimmed milk—5 calories

Lunch and Dinner Menus

Boiled Beef with Horseradish Sauce

> 3 *pounds lean beef* (*there will be leftovers*)
> 2 *large onions, sliced*
> 2 *bay leaves*
> 6 *peppercorns*
> 8 *large carrots*
> 2 *stalks celery with leaves, diced*
> *salt, pepper*

Cover meat with water. Add remaining ingredients. Simmer, covered, until tender, about 3 hours. Remove meat. Slice, heat in horseradish sauce, and serve surrounded by carrots and bouillon potatoes.

Horseradish Sauce (serves four)

> 1 *tablespoon butter*
> 1 *medium onion, diced*
> 2 *tablespoons flour*
> 2 *cups meat stock*
> ½ *cup freshly grated or prepared horseradish*
> 1 *tablespoon sugar*
> *salt, vinegar*
> *pinch ground cloves*

Sauté onion in butter until golden. Blend in flour. Add hot stock slowly, stirring constantly until thickened. Add horseradish, sugar, cloves, and salt and vinegar to taste.

Bouillon Potatoes

When meat is almost tender, add 4 pared potatoes, 2 inches in diameter. Cook until tender in stock with meat.

Lemon Cream Pie (serves eight)

> 13 *zwieback diet rusks*
> 2 *tablespoons butter melted*

1 *teaspoon cinnamon*
1 *package lemon Jello*
$\frac{1}{2}$ *cup water*
$\frac{1}{3}$ *cup sugar*
6 *tablespoons lemon juice*
grated rind of 1 lemon
$1\frac{1}{3}$ cups chilled evaporated milk

Crust—Grind rusks, using finest cutter of meat grinder. Mix with cinnamon and melted butter. Pat into pie plate.

Filling—Dissolve Jello and sugar in hot water. Add 4 tablespoons lemon juice. Cool. Whip chilled milk with remaining juice about 1 minute, or until consistency of whipped cream. Add Jello mixture and lemon rind. Whip until fluffy, about 2 minutes. Pour into crust and chill until firm.

Lunch and Dinner Menus

MENU 3

Luncheon—205 calories
Sautéed Mushrooms on Toast—200 calories
Coffee with saccharin and skimmed milk—5 calories

Sautéed Mushrooms on Toast

12 *medium-sized mushrooms ($\frac{1}{4}$ pound)*
1$\frac{1}{2}$ *teaspoons butter*
garlic
1 *small onion*
1 *tablespoon flour*
$\frac{1}{2}$ *cup bouillon*
1 *slice toast*
pinch marjoram
salt, pepper
1 *teaspoon chopped parsley*

Slice mushroom caps and stems. Cut onion into fine dice. Rub heavy iron frying pan with garlic. Melt butter. Sauté onions and mushrooms, shaking pan occasionally. When they are done, sprinkle with flour. Cook, stirring, for $\frac{1}{2}$ minute. Gradually add hot bouillon, blending well. Season with marjoram, salt and pepper. Cook 1 minute. Serve on hot toast. Garnish with parsley.

Dinner—705 calories
Roast Leg of Lamb—290 calories (3 slices
4$\frac{1}{2}$ inches by 2 inches by $\frac{1}{4}$ inch)
Peas à la Française—115 calories each portion
Glacéed Carrots—90 calories each portion
Molded Orange Sections—205 calories each portion
Coffee with skimmed milk and saccharin—5 calories

33

Roast Leg of Lamb

Small leg of lamb
1 *clove garlic*
1 *tablespoon salt*
1 *tablespoon curry powder*
pepper, pinch ginger
1 *onion*
1 *tablespoon Worcestershire sauce*

Place lamb in a roasting pan. Mash garlic with salt. Make gashes in meat and fill with mixture. Rub roast with curry powder, pepper and ginger. Sprinkle with Worcestershire sauce and slice onion on top of meat. Place in a 400° oven for 15 minutes. Add ½ cup of water to the pan. Turn heat to 325°. Cook about 2 hours all together, or until tender, basting every 15 minutes.

Note: Generally, when buying leg of lamb, I have the butcher prepare half for roasting, and cut the other half for Shish Kebab.

Peas à la Française (serves four)

2 *cups shelled peas*
2 *tablespoons butter*
1 *small onion, minced*
1 *small heart lettuce, shredded*
1 *teaspoon sugar*
½ *cup water*
salt, pepper

Place all ingredients in a pot. Cook slowly, covered, until tender, and most of the liquid has evaporated.

Glacéed Carrots (serves four)

4 *large carrots*
1 *tablespoon brown sugar*

1 *tablespoon lemon juice*
1 *teaspoon minced parsley*
2 *tablespoons butter*
dash paprika

Clean carrots and cut into julienne strips. Cook in boiling, salted water until tender. Drain well. Put back in pot with sugar, lemon juice, butter, paprika and parsley. Sauté for 5 minutes, shaking pot so that each piece will be coated.

Molded Orange Sections (serves four)

4 *medium oranges*
grated rind of 2 oranges
2 *cups orange juice*
1 *cup water*
6 *tablespoons sugar*
1½ *tablespoons gelatin*
4 *tablespoons lemon juice*

Peel oranges, separate sections and remove membrane. Sprinkle gelatin on ¼ cup cold water. Heat remaining water with fruit juices. Dissolve gelatin and sugar in it. Rinse a mold with cold water. Arrange half the orange sections in bottom. Add rind to gelatin mixture. Pour half over sections in mold. When mixture starts to thicken, arrange remaining orange sections in mold and cover with remaining gelatin. Chill.

MENU 4

Luncheon—215 calories
Roquefort and Cottage Cheese Salad—135 calories
Buttered Rye Toast—75 calories
Coffee with skimmed milk and saccharin—5 calories

Roquefort and Cottage Cheese Salad

 1 *medium tomato*
 1 *stalk celery*
 ½ *cucumber, sliced*
 5 *tablespoons cottage cheese*
 ½ *triangle Roquefort cheese (¾ oz.)*
 Worcestershire sauce
 caraway seeds

Mash Roquefort cheese. Blend with cotttage cheese. Add Worcestershire sauce to taste. Mound on serving dish. Surround with vegetables. Sprinkle seeds over cheese.

Buttered Rye Toast

Slice bread ⅜ inch thick. Toast one side under broiler. Spread other side with ½ teaspoon butter and broil.

Dinner—730 calories
Hungarian Chicken Paprika—230 calories each portion
Hungarian Egg Dumplings—250 calories each portion
1 cup Broccoli—45 calories
Old-Fashioned Strawberry Shortcake—200 calories
each portion
Coffee with skimmed milk and saccharin—5 calories

Hungarian Chicken Paprika (serves four)

 2 *medium broilers cut as for frying*
 3 *large onions, diced*

36

2 *tablespoons chicken fat*
½ *green pepper*
1 *tablespoon paprika*
salt, pepper
¼ *cup water*
¼ *cup sour cream*
1 *teaspoon flour*

Sauté onions in chicken fat in Dutch oven for three-quarters of an hour. Do not allow them to brown. Add green pepper and paprika. Add chicken pieces which have been washed but not dried, and seasonings. Add water. Cover and simmer until tender, about 45 minutes. Discard pepper. Remove chicken to serving platter. Blend sour cream mixed with flour into gravy, but do not boil. Pour over chicken.

Hungarian Egg Dumplings (serves four)

2 *eggs*
1 *tablespoon chicken fat*
1 *teaspoon salt*
½ *cup water*
1⅔ *cups flour*

Cream fat. Beat eggs. Mix with fat. Add salt, then flour and water alternately to make a thick elastic batter. Drop from a teaspoon, ⅓ spoon at a time, into rapidly boiling, salted water. Plunge spoon into the water each time, so that dough comes off. Cook about 7 minutes. Drain in colander. Rinse with cold water.

Broccoli

Remove large leaves and tough parts of stem. Gash bottom of the stems. Cook in boiling, salted water until tender. Drain well. A pinch of baking soda may be added to the water, while the vegetable is cooking, to maintain the fresh green color.

37

Old-Fashioned Strawberry Shortcake (serves six)

- $\frac{7}{8}$ *cup flour*
- $\frac{1}{2}$ *teaspoon salt*
- 1 *teaspoon baking powder*
- 2 *tablespoons butter and shortening, mixed*
- $\frac{1}{8}$ *cup skimmed milk*
- $\frac{1}{6}$ *cup water*
- 6 *tablespoons whipped cream*
- 3 *cups strawberries*
- $\frac{1}{4}$ *cup sugar*

Cut shortening and butter into sifted dry ingredients. Mix in liquid, working quickly. Knead dough on a board for $\frac{1}{2}$ minute. Roll dough out $\frac{3}{4}$ inch thick. Cut with biscuit cutter or glass into 6 biscuits. Bake on greased baking sheet at 425° for about 15 minutes or until lightly browned. Mash strawberries with sugar, reserving a few of the nicest for garnishing. Pour over biscuits, garnish with whole berries and top each portion with one tablespoon of whipped cream.

MENU 5

LUNCHEON—265 calories
½ cold Broiler—125 calories
String Bean Salad—60 calories
1 slice Rye Toast with ½ teaspoon butter—75 calories
Coffee with skimmed milk and saccharin—5 calories

Broiler

Left over from last night's Chicken Paprika. Serve without gravy.

String Bean Salad

½ *cup cooked string beans*
¼ *teaspoon grated onion*
1 *teaspoon oil*
1 *teaspoon vinegar*
2 *tablespoons string bean stock*
salt, pepper

Combine liquids, onion and seasonings to taste. Pour over beans and allow to marinate at least 1 hour before serving.

DINNER—645 calories
Swedish Stuffed Cabbage—300 calories each portion
⅔ cup Pickled Beets—75 calories
1 medium Boiled New Potato with Dill—45 calories
Gingerbread (3 inches by 2 inches by 1 inch) with
Whipped Cream—220 calories
Coffee with saccharin and skimmed milk—5 calories

Swedish Stuffed Cabbage (serves four)

8 *large cabbage leaves*
1 *pound lean chopped beef*

39

2 tablespoons raw rice
¾ cup skimmed milk
salt, pepper, nutmeg
2 tablespoons bacon fat
½ cup bouillon
½ cup whole milk

Parboil cabbage leaves 2 minutes or until pliable in boiling water. Cook rice in skimmed milk in top of double boiler until tender. Mix meat, cooked rice and seasonings. Divide the mixture among the eight leaves, placing it in the center of each leaf. Fold in the sides, and then roll up each leaf, enclosing the meat. Fry in fat in a Dutch oven to brown the rolls on all sides. Add bouillon and whole milk. Cover and finish cooking in a 375° oven for 1 hour.

Pickled Beets

See Menu 1.

New Potatoes with Dill

Cook medium-sized new potatoes with a touch of dill in boiling salted water to cover. Drain. Garnish with chopped fresh dill.

Gingerbread with Whipped Cream

Since the commercial mixes are so satisfactory and save work, I suggest using them. Therefore, I quote the caloric estimate given on the chart. Each slice of 3 inches by 2 inches by 1 inch is 150 calories. Serve slightly warm. Top each serving with 1¼ tablespoons whipped cream (1 tablespoon heavy cream) mixed with ½ teaspoon sugar.

MENU 6

Cold Lobster with Celery Root Salad—190 calories
2 Diet Bread Sticks—10 calories
Coffee with saccharin and skimmed milk—5 calories

Cold Lobster with Celery Root Salad

1 *medium-sized lobster or ⅔ cup lobster meat*
⅓ *cup cooked celery root*
1 *tablespoon diet mayonnaise*
1 *tablespoon chili sauce*
few drops lemon juice
vinegar
1 *onion*

Plunge a live lobster head first into briskly boiling salted water to cover. Boil 20 minutes. Cool quickly by plunging into cold water. Crack shell, discard intestinal vein. Pick out meat and arrange on serving dish. Peel celery root. Cook in boiling salted water with one onion for flavor. Dice and moisten with equal amounts of vinegar and vegetable stock. Serve lobster and celery root salad with Russian dressing, made of mayonnaise, chili sauce and lemon juice.

DINNER—730 calories

Cheese Soufflé—305 calories each portion
4 slices Crisp Bacon—100 calories
Carrot Sticks—15 calories each portion
Wilted Lettuce—90 calories each portion
Viennese Apple Kuchen—215 calories each portion
Coffee with saccharin and skimmed milk—5 calories

41

Cheese Soufflé (serves four)

> 2 *tablespoons butter*
> ⅓ *cup flour, scant*
> 1 *cup skimmed milk*
> 4 *eggs*
> 1 *cup grated American cheese*
> ¼ *teaspoon cream of tartar, salt, pepper*

Melt butter. Blend in flour. Gradually add hot milk, stirring constantly. Cook until thick. Add grated cheese. Separate eggs. Beat whites, with ½ teaspoon salt added, until foamy. Add cream of tartar and continue beating until stiff. Without washing beater, beat yolks until thick. Add yolks and a dash of pepper to sauce. Beat whole very well. Fold in stiffly beaten whites. Pour in greased pyrex baking dish. Set dish in pan of water in oven. Bake at 350° for 1 hour. Ten minutes before it is done, remove the pan of water. (This makes the soufflé puff up even more.)

Crisp Bacon

Place 16 slices of bacon in a cold heavy iron frying pan. Cook slowly, pouring off excess fat as it cooks. Drain on absorbent paper.

Carrot Sticks

Slice two large carrots in lengthwise, julienne strips. Place in ice water to crisp. This serves 4.

Wilted Lettuce (serves four)

> 1 *large head lettuce (Boston, preferably)*
> 2 *tablespoons chopped chives*
> 2 *sprigs dill, chopped*
> 3 *tablespoons bacon fat*
> 6 *tablespoons vinegar*

1½ *teaspoons sugar*
½ *teaspoon prepared mustard*
pinch pepper

Break lettuce into bite-size pieces in salad bowl. Sprinkle with chives and dill. Combine remaining ingredients. Cook 3 minutes. Pour over lettuce, toss well and serve immediately.

Viennese Apple Kuchen (serves eight)

½ *cake yeast*
¼ *cup skimmed milk*
1 *tablespoon sugar*
½ *teaspoon salt*
1 *egg, well beaten*
grated rind of 1 lemon
1 *cup flour*
6 *tablespoons melted butter*
3 *large cooking apples*
¼ *cup sugar*
1 *tablespoon cinnamon*

Scald milk and cool to lukewarm. Dissolve yeast in milk. Add 1 tablespoon sugar and salt. Let stand for 5 minutes. Add egg, rind, flour and butter. Beat well. Let stand 10 minutes. Knead on floured board until elastic and smooth. Cover and let rise in warm place until double in bulk. Punch down and roll out. Place on greased and floured 9-inch square or round baking pan. Let rise until almost double. Peel and core apples. Slice thin. Place slices on top of dough. Sprinkle with mixed sugar and cinnamon. Bake 35 to 40 minutes at 350°.

Reduce and Enjoy It Cookbook

MENU 7

LUNCHEON—225 calories
Cottage Cheese and Fruit Salad—210 calories
2 Diet Bread Sticks—10 calories
Coffee with skimmed milk and saccharin—5 calories

Cottage Cheese and Fruit Salad

> 2 *leaves lettuce*
> ⅓ *cup cottage cheese*
> 1 *tablespoon crushed pineapple*
> 2 *halves canned peaches, drained*
> 2 *cooked prunes, drained*
> ½ *orange*

Mix cottage cheese with crushed pineapple. Mound on lettuce. Surround with peaches, prunes and orange segments which have had the membrane removed.

DINNER—705 calories
Shish Kebab—425 calories each portion
Tomato Provençal—80 calories
Frozen Coffee Rum Soufflé—195 calories each portion
Coffee with skimmed milk and saccharin—5 calories

Shish Kebab (serves four)

> 24 *one-inch cubes leg of lamb (about 1½ pounds)*
> 2 *large onions, diced*
> 1 *teaspoon oregano*
> 1 *tablespoon salt*
> 1 *teaspoon black pepper*
> 2 *tablespoons oil*
> ⅓ *cup dry sherry*
> 12 *large mushroom caps*
> 12 *onions, 1-inch diameter*

44

Place meat in a bowl with the diced onions. Sprinkle with oregano, salt and pepper. Pour over it oil and sherry mixed. Allow meat to remain in this marinade for several hours, turning occasionally. Remove meat. Thread meat on skewers, alternating with a mushroom cap or an onion. Brush onions and mushrooms with any remaining marinade. Broil quite near flame. Turn to brown all sides.

Tomato Provençal

Use one good-sized tomato for each serving. Cut tomato in half, crosswise. Spread each half with $\frac{1}{2}$ teaspoon softened butter, 1 teaspoon breadcrumbs and a pinch each of salt, pepper and oregano. Set under broiler, not too near flame, and cook for about 5 minutes or until lightly browned and heated through.

Frozen Coffee Rum Soufflé (serves six)

> 1 *tablespoon gelatin*
> $\frac{1}{4}$ *cup cold water*
> $1\frac{1}{2}$ *cups strong hot coffee*
> $\frac{1}{3}$ *cup sugar*
> $\frac{1}{2}$ *cup milk*
> 3 *eggs*
> $\frac{1}{4}$ *cup sugar*
> $\frac{1}{2}$ *teaspoon vanilla*
> $\frac{1}{8}$ *teaspoon salt*
> $\frac{1}{4}$ *cup rum*
> $\frac{1}{4}$ *cup heavy cream*
> 12 *pecan halves*

Sprinkle gelatin on cold water. Soak for 3 minutes. Dissolve in the hot coffee. Add $\frac{1}{3}$ cup sugar and milk. Heat but do not boil. Pour a little over the egg yolks which have been mixed with the remaining sugar. Combine the two mixtures and cook, but do not boil, for a few minutes until slightly thick-ened. Add vanilla and rum. When cool and thick, fold in egg whites that have been stiffly beaten with salt. Pour in in-dividual serving dishes and chill. Garnish with whipped cream and chopped nut meats.

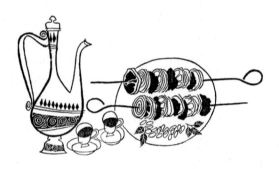

MENU 8

LUNCHEON—275 calories
Chicken Liver Paté Garni—230 calories
4 Diet Bread Sticks, ½ teaspoon butter—40 calories
Coffee with skimmed milk and saccharin—5 calories

Chicken Liver Paté Garni

1 *hard-boiled egg*
2 *chicken livers (2 ounces)*
1 *small onion*
1 *teaspoon chicken fat*
salt, pepper
2 *teaspoons diet mayonnaise*
2 *radishes, sliced*
½ *medium tomato, sliced*
3 *leaves lettuce*

Dice onion. Sauté onion and livers in fat. Chop egg with sautéed onion and liver until it reaches the consistency of a coarse paté. Blend in mayonnaise. Season to taste with salt and pepper. Mound on bed of lettuce and garnish with radishes and tomato.

DINNER—655 calories
Corned Beef—325 calories each portion of
⅓ pound cooked meat without fat
1 New Potato—45 calories
Savoy Cabbage—45 calories each portion (¼ head)
Chocolate Sundae—235 calories each portion
Coffee with skimmed milk and saccharin—5 calories

Corned Beef

> 3-4 *pounds corned beef (there will be leftovers)*
> 2 *bay leaves*
> 2 *onions*
> 6 *whole peppercorns*
> 1 *medium head savoy cabbage*
> 4 *new potatoes, 2-inch diameter*

Simmer corned beef with onions, peppercorns and bay leaves for 2 hours or until tender, in water to cover, changing first water if it tastes too salty. When almost done, add quartered head of cabbage and scrubbed, but not peeled, potatoes. Finish cooking together for about 15 minutes.

Chocolate Sundae (serves four)

> 2 *cups vanilla ice cream*
> 4 *tablespoons diet chocolate sauce*
> 2 *tablespoons strong hot coffee*
> 4 *marshmallows*

Dissolve marshmallows in coffee. Scoop ½ cup ice cream in each serving dish. Top each portion with 2 tablespoons chocolate sauce and marshmallow-coffee mixture.

Lunch and Dinner Menus

MENU 9

LUNCHEON—215 calories

Grilled Cheese and Tomato Sandwich—210 calories
Coffee with saccharin and skimmed milk—5 calories

Grilled Cheese and Tomato Sandwich

   2 *slices white bread*
   ½ *medium tomato, sliced*
   1 *slice American cheese (packaged slice)*

Toast one slice of bread on one side only; the other, on both
sides. Place tomato on untoasted side. Sprinkle with salt.
Place cheese on top of tomato, and set under broiler until
cheese melts. Top with the other slice of toast.

DINNER—720 calories

Deviled Crabmeat—245 calories each portion
Fresh Asparagus Tips Polonaise—105 calories each portion
Salad Imperial—140 calories each portion
Orange Chiffon Pie—225 calories each portion
Coffee with saccharin and skimmed milk—5 calories

Deviled Crabmeat (serves four)

   2⅔ *cups fresh or canned crabmeat*
   2 *teaspoons prepared mustard*
   5 *tablespoons breadcrumbs*
   6 *tablespoons skimmed milk*
   5 *tablespoons butter, melted*
   dash cayenne
   2 *tablespoons chopped parsley*
   1 *tablespoon lemon juice*
   2½ *teaspoons Worcestershire sauce*
   3 *tablespoons grated Parmesan cheese*

49

Combine all ingredients except cheese and 2½ tablespoons butter. Put in individual shallow baking dishes. Sprinkle cheese and remaining butter on top. Bake for 10 minutes in a 425° oven.

Fresh Asparagus Tips Polonaise (serves four)

> 48 *fresh or frozen asparagus tips*
> 2⅔ *tablespoons butter*
> 4 *teaspoons breadcrumbs*

Cook asparagus in boiling salted water until tender. Drain well. Pour breadcrumbs, browned in butter, over the vegetable.

Salad Imperial (serves four)

> 4 *hard-cooked eggs*
> 2 *teaspoons diet mayonnaise*
> 2 *teaspoons prepared mustard*
> 2 *cucumbers*
> 40 *pieces watercress (approx. 1 large bunch)*
> 28 *leaves romaine (approx. 1 medium head)*
> 4 *tablespoons diet mayonnaise*
> 4 *tablespoons skimmed milk*
> 2 *teaspoons lemon juice*
> 2 *teaspoons chopped chives*
> *salt, pepper, paprika*

Wash lettuce and cress. Drain and dry. Peel cucumbers and slice. Cut eggs in half, lengthwise. Mash yolks with 2 teaspoons mayonnaise and mustard. Refill egg whites, and sprinkle with paprika. Arrange a bed of lettuce in a salad bowl. Heap the cress in the center. Surround with the eggs and then the cucumber slices. Combine the mayonnaise, skimmed milk, lemon juice, chives and salt and pepper to taste. Pour over all.

Orange Chiffon Pie (serves eight)

> *Pie crust—See Lemon Cream Pie*
> 8 *eggs*
> ⅔ *cup juice* (½ *cup orange juice—the balance*
> *lemon juice*)
> ¼ *cup cold water*
> 1 *cup sugar*
> 1 *tablespoon gelatin*
> *rind of* 1 *lemon*
> *rind of* 1 *orange*

Sprinkle gelatin on cold water. Blend egg yolks, ½ cup sugar and fruit juice in top of double boiler. Cook over boiling water until thick. Add dissolved gelatin to hot custard. Cool. Add grated rinds. Beat egg whites until stiff. Add remaining sugar to beaten whites gradually, continuing to beat as you do so. Fold into cooled custard. Pile into pie crust. Chill in refrigerator.

MENU 10

Luncheon—215 calories
Corned Beef Sandwich on Rye Bread—175 calories
Cole Slaw—35 calories
Coffee with skimmed milk and saccharin—5 calories

Corned Beef Sandwich on Rye Bread

Place a slice of lean corned beef on one slice of bread, which has been spread with ½ teaspoon mustard. Cover with two leaves of lettuce, and top with other slice of bread.

Cole Slaw

> ½ *cup shredded cabbage*
> 1 *strip green pepper, diced*
> 1 *teaspoon grated carrot*
> ¼ *teaspoon grated onion*
> 2 *teaspoons diet mayonnaise*
> 2 *teaspoons skimmed milk*
> *salt, few drops lemon juice*

Combine cabbage, diced green pepper, carrot and onion. Blend mayonnaise, milk, lemon juice and salt. Mix with slaw.

Dinner—715 calories
Filet of Sole Soufflé—410 calories each portion
Minted Fresh Peas—55 calories each portion
Fresh Strawberry Sundae—245 calories each portion
Coffee with saccharin and skimmed milk—5 calories

Filet of Sole Soufflé (serves four)

> 2 *pounds filet of sole*
> *bones and heads of fish*
> 1 *onion*

bay leaf, 2 peppercorns
¾ cup white wine
1½ cups water
salt, pepper
4 potatoes, 4 inches by 2 inches
½ cup skimmed milk
3 eggs, separated
2 tablespoons butter
4 tablespoons flour
2 cups fish stock
juice of ½ lemon
4 tablespoons Parmesan cheese

Place fish bones and heads in a pot with water, wine, onion, bay leaf, peppercorns and salt. Simmer for ½ hour. Strain stock. Cook fish gently in the stock for 5 or 6 minutes. Peel and boil potatoes. Mash them with milk, salt to taste and one egg yolk. Make a bed of potatoes on a flat, greased baking dish. Lay well-drained fish filets on top. Melt butter, blend in flour and gradually add hot fish stock, stirring constantly until thickened. Cool slightly. Add two egg yolks, lemon juice and salt and pepper to taste. Beat egg whites until stiff. Fold into half the sauce and spread over fish. Sprinkle with grated cheese and place in a 450° oven to brown. Serve, with the balance of the sauce on the side.

Minted Fresh Peas

Boil 2 cups shelled fresh peas in water, with 1 teaspoon sugar and a small bunch of fresh mint. Drain, and serve with chopped blanched mint leaves. Serves 4.

Fresh Strawberry Sundae (serves four)

> 1 *pint vanilla ice cream*
> 2 *cups fresh strawberries*
> 1 *tablespoon sugar*

Reserve 1 cup of the best berries. Mash the other cup with sugar. Pour sauce over ice cream in individual dishes and top with fresh berries.

Lunch and Dinner Menus

MENU 11

LUNCHEON—225 calories
Western Omelet—220 calories
Coffee with saccharin and skimmed milk—5 calories

Western Omelet

2 *eggs*
1 *slice lean boiled ham (4 inches by 2 inches by ⅛ inch)*
1 *small onion*
⅛ *green pepper*
2 *tablespoons water*
1 *teaspoon butter*
salt, pepper

Dice ham, onions and green pepper. Sauté gently in ½ teaspoon butter in heavy iron frying pan. Beat eggs and water until well blended. Mix in cooked ham, vegetables and seasonings. Heat pan with remaining butter. Pour in egg mixture. Turn heat low. Lift the edges of the omelet with a spatula to permit the uncooked portion to go to the bottom. When it is cooked to desired degree of firmness, fold over and serve.

DINNER—705 calories
Roast Veal—365 calories (4 slices 4 inches
by 3 inches by ¼ inch)
Hungarian Sauerkraut—100 calories each portion
Whipped Potatoes—85 calories each portion
Chocolate Cream Puff, Chocolate Sauce—
150 calories each portion
Coffee with saccharin and skimmed milk—5 calories

Roast Veal

3-4 *pound rump or leg of veal, boned and rolled*
1 *clove garlic*

1 *tablespoon salt*
pepper, paprika, ginger
3 *strips bacon*
1 *large onion, sliced*

Place veal in roasting pan. Mash garlic with salt. Rub into veal. Sprinkle with pepper, paprika and ginger. Lay bacon strips on meat. Cover with sliced onion. Pour ½ cup water in pan. Roast at 375° for 1½ to 2 hours, or until tender, basting every fifteen minutes.

Hungarian Sauerkraut (serves four)

2 *cups sauerkraut*
⅔ *cup tomato sauce*
3 *large onions, diced*
1 *tablespoon water*
1 *tablespoon flour*

Put sauerkraut, onions and tomato sauce in saucepan. Add enough water just to cover. Simmer over slow flame for 1 hour. Thicken juice slightly with flour and water mixed to a paste.

Whipped Potatoes (serves four)

3 *potatoes (2 inches by 4 inches)*
¾ *cup skimmed milk*
2 *tablespoons chopped chives*
salt, pepper

Cook potatoes in boiling salted water until tender. Put through ricer. Blend in hot milk, chives and salt and pepper to taste. Whip until fluffy and light.

Chocolate Cream Puffs, Chocolate Sauce (serves five)

2 *tablespoons butter*
¼ *cup boiling water*
¼ *cup flour*
1 *egg*

5 *tablespoons heavy cream*
$\frac{1}{2}$ *teaspoon sugar*
5 *tablespoons diet chocolate sauce*

Bring butter and water to a boil in a small saucepan. Add flour. Stir vigorously. Remove from fire as soon as it is mixed. Add egg and beat with a wooden spoon for 3 minutes. Drop batter in 5 equal portions on a greased baking sheet, 2 inches apart, making them as circular as possible. Bake in a 375° oven for $\frac{1}{2}$ hour. To test, take one from pan. If it does not fall, they are done. Cool. Whip cream until stiff. Fold in sugar. Split cream puffs. Fill with cream. Serve with chocolate sauce as topping.

MENU 12

Luncheon—205 calories
Chef's Salad—165 calories
3 Diet Bread Sticks, ½ teaspoon butter—35 calories
Coffee with skimmed milk and saccharin—5 calories

Chef's Salad

1 *slice lean boiled ham (4 inches by 2 inches by ⅛ inch)*
1 *slice chicken (4 inches by 2 inches by ⅛ inch)*
½ *medium slice Swiss cheese*
5 *medium slices cucumber*
2 *radishes, sliced*
Iceberg, romaine, escarole lettuce
1 *tablespoon diet mayonnaise*
1 *tablespoon skimmed milk*
1 *teaspoon chili sauce*
1 *teaspoon chopped chives*
few drops lemon juice

Cut ham, chicken and cheese in julienne strips. Break lettuce into bite-size pieces. Salt lettuce well. Mix in radishes and cucumber. Arrange in salad bowl. Lay strips of meat and cheese on top. Pour over dressing of mayonnaise, milk, chili sauce and lemon juice. Garnish with chives.

Dinner—720 calories

Curried Shrimp—275 calories
Saffron Rice—215 calories
Cucumber Salad—60 calories
Camembert Cheese with Fresh Pear—165 calories
Coffee with skimmed milk and saccharin—5 calories

Curried Shrimp (serves four)

2 *pounds shrimp*
1 *large onion*
3 *tablespoons butter*
6 *tablespoons flour*
1 *tablespoon curry powder*
1¼ *teaspoons salt*
1½ *teaspoons sugar*
¼ *teaspoon ginger*
1 *cup bouillon*
2 *cups skimmed milk*
1 *teaspoon lemon juice*

Cook shrimp about 5 minutes in boiling water. Peel and devein. Sauté minced onion in butter. Stir in flour, curry powder, salt, sugar and ginger. Add hot bouillon and milk, stirring constantly until thick. Add lemon juice. Combine shrimp with sauce and heat thoroughly.

Saffron Rice (serves four)

¾ *cup raw rice*
1 *tablespoon oil*
2 *tablespoons butter*
small clove garlic, minced
½ *teaspoon saffron*
bouillon
2 *tablespoons grated Parmesan cheese*

Melt oil and butter. Sauté garlic for 1 minute. Add rice and sauté, stirring constantly for 3 minutes. Cover with bouillon to 1 inch above rice and bring to a boil. Add saffron, salt and pepper. Cover pot with waxed paper and lid. Finish cooking in 325° oven for about ½ hour. Stir in cheese.

Cucumber Salad (serves four)

- 2 *cucumbers*
- 1 *teaspoon salt*
- 2 *tablespoons sugar*
- 2 *teaspoons oil*
- 4 *tablespoons vinegar*
- 2 *teaspoons chopped parsley*

Slice cucumbers paper thin. Salt and let stand for $\frac{1}{2}$ hour. Squeeze out most of liquid. Combine sugar, vinegar and oil, and pour over cucumbers. Garnish with chopped parsley.

Camembert Cheese with Fresh Pear

This cheese is sold in $1\frac{1}{3}$-ounce wedges. Use one wedge for each portion. Serve cheese at room temperature. Peel and slice each pear into 8 slices. Cheese should be eaten spread on slice of fruit.

MENU 13

Luncheon—205 calories
Tomato Stuffed with Crabmeat—125 calories
1 Slice Rye Toast with ½ teaspoon butter—75 calories
Coffee with saccharin and skimmed milk—5 calories

Tomato Stuffed with Crabmeat

> 1 *large tomato, scooped out and drained*
> ½ *cup crabmeat*
> 1 *stalk celery*
> 3 *leaves lettuce*
> 1 *tablespoon diet mayonnaise*
> 1 *tablespoon skimmed milk*
> 1 *teaspoon chopped chives*
> *salt, few drops lemon juice*

Dice celery and mix with crabmeat. Blend mayonnaise, milk, lemon juice, chives and salt. Combine with crabmeat mixture. Fill tomato shell and serve on lettuce.

Dinner—705 calories
Pot Roast in Red Wine—450 calories each portion
(allowing 2 tablespoons gravy for each)
Mixed Vegetable Salad—100 calories each portion
Fruits Rafraîchis—150 calories each portion
Coffee with saccharin and skimmed milk—5 calories

Pot Roast in Red Wine (serves four)

> Marinade: 2 *onions, diced*
> 1 *carrot, diced*
> 2 *cloves*
> 2 *bay leaves*
> 1 *clove garlic, minced*

61

10 *peppercorns*
3 *sprigs parsley*
1 *cup red wine*
$\frac{1}{4}$ *cup oil*
2 *tablespoons vinegar*

Mix all the above ingredients in a bowl. Soak the meat in it for 24 hours, turning occasionally.

$2\frac{1}{2}$-*pound piece of bottom round*
$1\frac{1}{2}$ *tablespoons butter*
2 *tablespoons sherry*
12 *small white onions*
$\frac{1}{2}$ *pound mushrooms, sliced*
1 *teaspoon chili sauce*
1 *teaspoon meat concentrate*
2 *tablespoons flour*
1 *cup bouillon*
1 *cup red wine*
salt, pepper
pinch basil

Remove meat from marinade and dry. Brown in roasting pan in butter. Pour sherry over meat. Remove meat. Brown onions in the pan. Add mushrooms. Cook for 3 minutes. Add chili sauce, meat concentrate and flour. Add bouillon gradually, stirring constantly until it comes to a boil. Add the wine, then the meat, herbs and seasonings. Cover and cook in a 350° oven for $1\frac{1}{2}$ hours. Remove meat. Slice, put back in pot and finish cooking until tender. Arrange meat on serving platter, surrounded by onions and mushrooms. Serve gravy separately in a sauce boat.

Mixed Vegetable Salad (serves four)

8 *leaves lettuce*
2 *carrots, cut in julienne strips*

1 *cup shelled peas*
2 *cups string beans, frenched*
1 *small onion, grated*
2 *tablespoons chili sauce*
3 *tablespoons skimmed milk*
2 *tablespoons diet mayonnaise*
1 *teaspoon lemon juice*
salt

Cook vegetables separately. Drain and chill. Arrange in mounds on lettuce. Combine chili sauce, milk, mayonnaise, onion, lemon juice and salt. Pour dressing over salad.

Fruits Rafraîchis (serves four)

1 *medium banana*
1 *grapefruit*
1 *medium orange*
2 *slices pineapple ¾ inch thick*
1 *large apple*
2 *tablespoons sugar*
1 *cordial glass Kirsch*

Peel grapefruit and orange. Separate sections and remove membrane. Peel pineapple and apple. Dice. Combine these fruits with sugar. Pour Kirsch over fruit. Chill for at least an hour. Just before serving mix in sliced banana.

MENU 14

Chive Cheese and Cucumber Sandwich—215 calories
Coffee with skimmed milk and saccharin—5 calories

Chive Cheese and Cucumber Sandwich

> 2 *slices white bread, toasted*
> 2 *tablespoons chive cheese*
> 5 *medium slices cucumber*
> 1 *teaspoon diet mayonnaise*
> $\frac{1}{2}$ *teaspoon onion salt*
> *lettuce leaf*

Spread toast with mayonnaise and cheese. Sprinkle with onion salt. Cover with cucumber slices and lettuce, and top with other slice of toast.

DINNER—700 calories

Spaghetti with Italian Meat Sauce—535 calories
each portion
Salad Parma—55 calories each portion
Minted Pineapple Glacé—105 calories each portion
Coffee with saccharin and skimmed milk—5 calories

Spaghetti with Italian Meat Sauce (serves four)

> 6 *cups cooked spaghetti (increase the amount if using diet spaghetti)*
> 4 *strips lean bacon*
> 2 *large onions*
> 1 *pound lean ground beef*
> 4 *cloves garlic, minced*
> 3 *tablespoons parsley, finely chopped*
> 1 *teaspoon salt*

freshly ground black pepper
½ teaspoon dry crushed red pepper
2 ounces red wine
1 cup tomato juice
1¼ cups tomato sauce
2 stalks celery, finely chopped
1 small carrot, finely diced

Sauté bacon until crisp. Drain on absorbent paper. Discard all but 2 tablespoons bacon fat. Sauté onion until golden, add beef and continue cooking until both are brown, stirring occasionally. Add garlic, parsley, salt, pepper and red pepper. Cook slowly for 10 minutes. Add wine, tomato juice and sauce. Bring to a boil. Add celery, carrot and crumbled bacon. Cover and simmer for 1 hour. Pour over spaghetti, which has been cooked until just tender in boiling salted water and drained.

Salad Parma (serves four)

4 hearts artichoke
escarole, lettuce
12 stalks endive
2 tablespoons diet mayonnaise
2 tablespoons skimmed milk
1 teaspoon lemon juice
1 teaspoon chopped chives
1 teaspoon parsley
salt

Break lettuce and escarole in bite-size pieces in salad bowl. Salt well. Place artichoke hearts on top, surrounded by endive. Pour over dressing of mayonnaise, milk, lemon juice and chives. Garnish with parsley.

Minted Pineapple Glacé

    8 *slices ripe fresh pineapple ½ inch thick*
    2 *cordial glasses Crème de Menthe*
    2 *tablespoons chopped fresh mint leaves*

Dice fresh pineapple. Pour liqueur over fruit and allow to rest in it for at least 1 hour. Serve in fruit cups over chopped ice. Garnish with mint leaves.

Lunch and Dinner Menus

MENU 15

<small>Luncheon</small>—215 calories
Herb Omelet—175 calories
Carrot Sticks (½ large carrot)—15 calories
4 Diet Bread Sticks—20 calories
Coffee with saccharin and skimmed milk—5 calories

Herb Omelet

2 *eggs*
2 *tablespoons water*
1 *teaspoon butter*
1 *tablespoon chopped parsley*
1 *tablespoon chopped chives*
pinch basil
salt, pepper

Beat eggs and water until well blended. Add seasonings and
herbs. Melt butter in a heavy iron frying pan. Pour in egg mixture. Turn heat low. Lift the edges of the omelet with a
spatula to permit the uncooked portion to go to the bottom.
When it is cooked to desired degree of firmness, fold over and
serve.

<small>Dinner</small>—705 calories
Lobster Farci—345 calories each portion
Baked Stuffed Potato—110 calories each portion
Asparagus Vinaigrette—70 calories each portion
Sponge Cake—175 calories each portion
Coffee with saccharin and skimmed milk—5 calories

Lobster Farci (serves four)

4 *medium-sized lobsters*
2 *tablespoons butter*

67

4 *tablespoons flour*
1 *cup chicken bouillon or one cube dissolved in water*
1 *cup skimmed milk*
2 *egg yolks*
1 *tablespoon dry mustard*
2 *tablespoons chopped parsley*
salt, pepper
¾ *cup grated Parmesan cheese*

Cook lobsters as in Menu 6. Remove meat carefully, keeping body of the shell intact. Melt butter, blend in flour and add hot milk and bouillon gradually, stirring constantly until thickened. Cool slightly. Add egg yolks, mustard, parsley, salt and pepper. Mix with lobster meat. Refill shells, sprinkle with cheese and place in a 400° oven until lightly browned. The same recipe may be used with fresh or canned lobster meat. Allow ⅔ cup meat for one serving. Bake in small, flat, individual baking dishes.

Baked Stuffed Potato (serves four)

4 *potatoes (2 inches by 4 inches)*
¾ *cup skimmed milk*
2 *tablespoons chopped chives*
salt, pepper, paprika

Bake potatoes. Cut a thin slice from the flat side of each potato. Carefully scoop out potatoes. Mash. Add hot milk, chives and salt and pepper to taste. Whip until light and fluffy. Refill shells, and sprinkle top liberally with paprika.

Asparagus Vinaigrette (serves four)

32 *asparagus*
2 *tablespoons salad oil*
2 *tablespoons vinegar*
1 *teaspoon minced onion*

1 *teaspoon minced parsley*
1 *tablespoon minced green pepper*
salt, pepper, pinch sugar

Cut off tough ends of vegetable. Tie in bunches and cook in boiling salted water to cover. Drain and chill. Serve with a vinaigrette dressing of the balance of the ingredients well blended.

Sponge Cake (serves ten)

6 *eggs, separated*
1 *cup sugar*
2 *tablespoons lemon juice*
grated rind of one orange
1 *cup cake flour*
1 *teaspoon baking powder*
¼ *teaspoon salt*

Beat egg yolks and sugar until thick and lemon colored. Add juice and rind. Sift flour, salt and baking powder three times. Fold in alternately with stiffly beaten whites. Pour into greased and floured 10-inch tube pan. Bake at 350° for about 45 minutes.

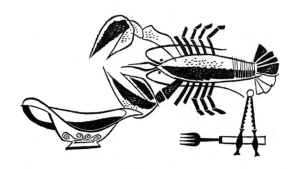

MENU 16

<small>Luncheon—235 calories</small>
Sardine Sandwich—195 calories
Cauliflower Salad—35 calories
Coffee with saccharin and skimmed milk—5 calories

Sardine Sandwich

> 2 *slices bread*
> 4 *small or 2 large sardines, well drained of oil*
> *few drops lemon juice*
> *few drops Worcestershire sauce*
> 1 *leaf lettuce*
> 1 *teaspoon diet mayonnaise*

Toast bread. Spread one slice with mayonnaise. Arrange sardines on toast, sprinkle with lemon juice and Worcestershire sauce. Top with lettuce and other slice of toast.

Cauliflower Salad

> ½ *cup cooked or raw cauliflower*
> 1 *teaspoon diet mayonnaise*
> 1 *teaspoon chili sauce*
> 2 *leaves lettuce*

Arrange cauliflower on lettuce. (Try it raw. It's exceptionally good.) Pour over dressing of mayonnaise blended with chili sauce.

<small>Dinner—675 calories</small>
Chicken in Wine, Fines Herbes—250 calories each portion
Corn on the Cob—105 calories each
String Beans Almondine—115 calories each portion
Prune Whip—200 calories each portion
Coffee with saccharin and skimmed milk—5 calories

Chicken in Wine, Fines Herbes (serves four)

2 medium-sized broilers
4 tablespoons butter
salt, pepper
¾ cup white wine
2 tablespoons chopped parsley
2 tablespoons chopped chives
1 tablespoon chopped fresh tarragon or ½ teaspoon dried
½ tablespoon chopped fresh thyme or ¼ teaspoon dried.

Have chickens cut as for frying. Season with salt and pepper. Melt butter in a heavy iron frying pan. Brown chicken pieces. Add wine and herbs. Cover pan, and simmer slowly until tender, about ½ hour.

Corn on the Cob

Cook 4 good-sized ears of fresh or frozen corn in boiling water to which 1 tablespoon sugar has been added. Do not overcook.

String Beans Almondine (serves four)

3 cups cooked frenched string beans
2 tablespoons butter
15 almonds

Use either fresh or frozen vegetable. Cook in boiling salted water until just tender. Drain well. Blanch almonds by putting in very hot water for a few minutes until skins slip off easily. Sliver nuts, and sauté in butter until golden. (Watch carefully, as they burn easily.) Pour almonds and butter over beans, and serve.

Prune Whip (serves four)

1 pound prunes or 1 cup thick prune pulp
1 cinnamon stick
5 egg whites

$\frac{1}{8}$ *teaspoon salt*
$\frac{1}{4}$ *teaspoon cream of tartar*
$\frac{1}{2}$ *cup sugar*
1 *teaspoon grated lemon rind*

Soak prunes and cinnamon stick in hot water to cover for 1 hour. In same water, boil slowly for $\frac{1}{2}$ hour. Drain and pit prunes. Put pulp through a ricer. Add sugar and lemon rind. Beat egg whites and salt until foamy. Add cream of tartar and beat until stiff. Fold into prune pulp. Place in a greased 9-inch baking dish. Set in a pan of hot water. Bake in a 275° oven for 1 hour, or until firm.

Lunch and Dinner Menus

MENU 17

LUNCHEON—230 calories
Eggs au Beurre Noir—190 calories
Asparagus Tip Salad—35 calories
Coffee with skimmed milk and saccharin—5 calories

Eggs au Beurre Noir

2 *eggs*
1½ *teaspoons butter*
1 *teaspoon wine or herb vinegar*
4 *or* 5 *capers*

Melt ½ teaspoon butter in heavy iron frying pan. When pan is hot, break eggs into it. Turn heat low. Sauté eggs. Remove to serving dish. Add remaining butter to pan and brown. Add vinegar and capers. Heat through, and pour over eggs.

Asparagus Tip Salad

5 *canned white asparagus tips*
2 *leaves lettuce*
1 *teaspoon chili sauce*
1 *teaspoon diet mayonnaise*

Blend chili sauce and mayonnaise. Pour over asparagus tips on lettuce.

DINNER—700 calories
Baked Ham with Mustard Sauce—330 calories
(4 slices 4 inches by 4 inches by ⅛ inch and ¼ cup sauce)
Baked Acorn Squash—95 calories each portion
Creamed Spinach—70 calories each portion
Grandma's Rice Pudding—200 calories each portion
Coffee with saccharin and skimmed milk—5 calories

73

Baked Ham with Mustard Sauce

> *small half smoked ham, boned and rolled*
> *cloves*
> *gingerale*
> *1 tablespoon butter*
> *2 tablespoons flour*
> *1 cup stock*
> *prepared mustard*

Bake ham as directed on package. The cooking will depend on the type of ham, and the amount of precooking that has been done. I always use the precooked type, which only requires browning. For this, I score the fat, stud with cloves and place in a 375° oven. Cook the ham for about three-quarters of an hour, or until nicely browned, basting occasionally with gingerale. Slice and serve with hot mustard sauce.

Sauce—Melt butter, blend in flour, and gradually add hot stock, stirring constantly until thickened. Add mustard to taste.

Baked Acorn Squash (serves four)

> *2 medium squash*
> *4 teaspoons brown sugar*
> *2 teaspoons butter*
> *dash nutmeg*
> *1 teaspoon grated orange rind*

Cut squash in halves and remove seeds. Put 1 teaspoon brown sugar, ½ teaspoon butter, dash of nutmeg and ¼ teaspoon orange rind in each. Place on baking sheet. Bake at 375° for about three-quarters of an hour, basting occasionally with the syrup in the squash.

Creamed Spinach (serves four)

> *3 cups cooked spinach (about 4 pounds)*
> *½ cup skimmed milk*

74

½ *cup spinach water*
2 *teaspoons bacon fat*
1 *tablespoon flour*
salt, pepper

Wash spinach carefully in several waters. Put it, still moist, in a pan without additional water. Cook until tender, about 5 minutes. Chop fine. Melt bacon fat, blend in flour, and add hot milk and spinach water, stirring constantly until thickened. Fold into chopped spinach. Add salt and pepper to taste.

Grandma's Rice Pudding (serves five)

6 *tablespoons raw rice*
6 *tablespoons sugar*
1½ *teaspoons vanilla*
5 *cups skimmed milk*
1 *teaspoon nutmeg*
pinch salt

Wash rice very thoroughly. Put all ingredients in a greased baking dish. Bake at 400°, stirring every 20 minutes for 1¾ hours, or until pudding is of creamy consistency. Serve at room temperature.

Reduce and Enjoy It Cookbook

MENU 18

LUNCHEON—270 calories
Curried Chopped Egg Salad—190 calories
Slice Rye Toast with ½ teaspoon butter—75 calories
Coffee with saccharin and skimmed milk—5 calories

Curried Chopped Egg Salad

> 2 *hard-boiled eggs*
> 3 *leaves lettuce*
> 1 *medium tomato*
> 1 *tablespoon diet mayonnaise*
> *curry powder, salt*

Put eggs through ricer. Mix with mayonnaise. Add curry powder and salt to taste. Mound on bed of lettuce. Surround with tomato wedges.

DINNER—660 calories
Coquilles St. Jacques—350 calories each
8 Fresh Asparagus Tips—20 calories
⅓ cup Lima Beans—80 calories
Angel Cake with Crushed Raspberries—205 calories
each portion
Coffee with saccharin and skimmed milk—5 calories

Coquilles St. Jacques (serves four)

> 1 *pound scallops*
> ¾ *cup white wine*
> *few sprigs parsley, celery leaves, 1 onion*
> ¼ *pound mushrooms*
> 1 *onion, diced*
> 5 *tablespoons butter*
> ¼ *cup water*

76

1½ *tablespoons lemon juice*
⅓ *teaspoon salt, pinch pepper, pinch thyme*
3 *tablespoons flour*
2 *egg yolks*
½ *cup skimmed milk*
¼ *cup breadcrumbs*

Simmer scallops gently in wine with parsley, celery leaves and whole onion for 5 minutes. Drain, reserving liquid. Cut scallops into small pieces. Chop mushrooms fine. Cook mushrooms with diced onion for 5 minutes in water, 2 tablespoons butter, lemon juice, salt, pepper and thyme. Drain, reserving liquid. Melt 2 tablespoons butter, add flour and gradually add both liquids, stirring until thickened. Add egg yolks, milk, scallops and mushroom-onion mixture. Stir until well thickened, but do not boil. Divide mixture among 4 shells. Moisten breadcrumbs with remaining tablespoon butter melted, and sprinkle over coquilles. Brown under broiler.

Fresh Asparagus Tips

Use either fresh or frozen vegetable. Boil in salted water until tender. Drain. Sprinkle liberally with freshly ground black pepper.

Lima Beans

Cook frozen vegetable as directed on package, or cook fresh beans in boiling salted water to cover about 15 minutes, or until tender.

Angel Cake with Crushed Raspberries (serves twelve)

1¼ *cups egg whites (about 10)*
1½ *cups sifted sugar*
1 *cup plus 2 tablespoons flour*
1 *teaspoon vanilla*

½ *teaspoon almond extract*
¼ *teaspoon salt*
1¼ *teaspoons cream of tartar*

Sift flour with ½ cup sugar 4 times. Beat egg whites and salt until foamy. Add cream of tartar. Continue beating until stiff but moist. Add remaining sugar, one-quarter at a time. Fold in flour and sugar mixture, one-quarter at a time. Bake in ungreased 10-inch tube pan 30 to 35 minutes at 375°. Remove pan, invert on wire rack and let cool for 1 hour before removing cake. For sauce for each portion, crush ⅓ cup raspberries with 1 teaspoon sugar.

Note: There are now some excellent prepared angel cake mixes on the market. A lot less trouble, and just as good.

MENU 19

LUNCHEON—275 calories
Soufflé Omelet Parmesan—200 calories
1 Slice White Toast with ½ teaspoon butter—70 calories
Coffee with saccharin and skimmed milk—5 calories

Soufflé Omelet Parmesan

2 *eggs*
2 *tablespoons skimmed milk*
½ *teaspoon baking powder*
2 *tablespoons Parmesan cheese, grated*
½ *teaspoon butter*
salt

Beat egg yolks with milk and baking powder. Add a pinch of salt. Beat egg whites stiff. Fold into yolk mixture. Melt butter in heavy iron pan. Have pan quite hot. Pour in egg mixture and turn flame low. Sprinkle cheese on top. Cover. Cook over low heat about 5 minutes, cutting through omelet with a knife, from time to time, to permit heat to penetrate.

DINNER—675 calories
Chicken livers and Mushrooms Sauté—325 calories
each portion
½ cup Boiled Rice—80 calories
Artichoke with Russian Dressing—120 calories
Baked Peaches with Meringue—145 calories
Coffee with saccharin and skimmed milk—5 calories

Chicken Livers and Mushrooms Sauté (serves four)

1¼ *pounds chicken livers*
¼ *pound mushrooms, sliced*
2 *tablespoons butter*

1 *medium onion, grated*
1 *tablespoon flour*
$\frac{1}{2}$ *cup chicken bouillon (or cube dissolved in water)*
$\frac{1}{2}$ *cup dry white wine*
bay leaf, pinch thyme
salt, pepper, nutmeg
1 *tablespoon chopped parsley*

Sauté livers and mushrooms in butter over a low flame. Add onion. Cook for 3 or 4 minutes, stirring. Sprinkle with flour, and add bouillon and wine, stirring constantly. Add bay leaf, thyme, salt and pepper. Cover and simmer for 10 minutes, stirring occasionally. Pour into serving dish. Sprinkle with a little nutmeg, and garnish with parsley.

Boiled Rice

Allow 2 tablespoons raw rice for each serving. Boil in salted water until tender, about 20 minutes. Drain in colander, rinse with cold water, and set in oven to dry out thoroughly.

Note: I often use the precooked rice that is on the market. I find it highly satisfactory.

Artichoke with Russian Dressing

Cut off the bottom portion of the stem. Cook in boiling salted water to cover. Add 1 tablespoon vinegar to water. Cook until tender, about 45 minutes. Drain and chill. Serve cold with a dressing made of 1 tablespoon diet mayonnaise and 2 teaspoons chili sauce.

Baked Peaches with Meringue (serves three)

6 *canned peach halves drained (or fresh stewed fruit)*
1 *tablespoon brown sugar*
$\frac{1}{2}$ *tablespoon butter, melted*
1 *teaspoon lemon juice*
$\frac{1}{4}$ *cup sweet sherry*

1 *egg white*
2 *tablespoons sugar*
1 *teaspoon water*
pinch salt
pinch cream of tartar
⅓ *teaspoon almond extract*

Place peach halves, cut side up in a pyrex pie plate. Mix brown sugar, butter and lemon juice. Fill the peach cavities with the mixture. Pour wine over the fruit. Beat egg white, water and salt until foamy. Add cream of tartar. Beat until stiff but moist. Beat in sugar, 1 teaspoon at a time, then almond extract. Top each peach with a portion of the meringue. Bake in 350° oven for 15 to 20 minutes, or until lightly browned.

Note: This recipe is equally successful with pears or apples.

Reduce and Enjoy It Cookbook

MENU 20

Luncheon—220 calories
Shrimp Salad—140 calories
1 Slice Rye Toast with ½ teaspoon butter—75 calories
Coffee with saccharin and skimmed milk—5 calories

Shrimp Salad

> ⅔ *cup cooked and cleaned shrimp*
> 1 *stalk celery*
> 3 *leaves lettuce*
> 1 *tablespoon diet mayonnaise*
> 1 *tablespoon skimmed milk*
> 1 *teaspoon chopped chives*
> *salt, pepper*
> *few drops lemon juice*

Cook raw shrimp for 8 minutes in boiling, slightly acidulated water (1 tablespoon vinegar to 1 quart water). Cool, peel and de-vein. Cut shrimp in halves or thirds. Mix with finely diced celery. Arrange on lettuce. Pour over dressing made of mayonnaise, skimmed milk, lemon juice, chives, salt and pepper.

Dinner—705 calories
Chicken Fricassee—320 calories each portion
¾ cup Steamed Rice—120 calories
Peas and Carrots—55 calories each portion
Marble Cup Cake with Chocolate Sauce—205 calories each portion
Coffee with saccharin and skimmed milk—5 calories

Chicken Fricassee (serves four)

> 1 *5-pound fowl*
> 3 *carrots, diced*

82

4 *stalks celery, diced*
3 *whole onions*
2 *bay leaves*
6 *peppercorns*
3 *tablespoons chopped parsley*
2 *egg yolks*
2 *tablespoons chicken fat*
4 *tablespoons flour*
juice of ½ lemon
salt, pepper

Cover fowl with boiling water. Add carrots, celery, onions, bay leaves, peppercorns and salt. Cook slowly until tender, about 2½ hours. Cut into portions, remove skin and place on serving platter and cover with the following sauce. Melt chicken fat, blend in flour and add 2 cups hot stock gradually, stirring constantly until thickened. Add seasonings, juice, parsley and egg yolks. Heat through, but do not boil.

Peas and Carrots

2 *large carrots, sliced*
1½ *cups shelled peas*
1 *teaspoon sugar*
¼ *teaspoon salt*
½ *teaspoon lemon juice*
pinch paprika

Cook carrots. Cook peas in boiling water with 1 teaspoon sugar. Drain both vegetables and combine them. Add salt, lemon juice and paprika.

Marble Cup Cakes with Chocolate Sauce (serves six)

⅛ *cup butter*
7 *tablespoons sugar*
1 *egg, well beaten*

83

⅔ *cup flour*
1⅓ *teaspoons baking powder*
pinch salt
⅙ *cup skimmed milk*
2 *teaspoons cocoa*
⅓ *teaspoon vanilla*
⅓ *teaspoon almond extract*
¾ *cup diet chocolate sauce*

Cream butter and sugar. Add egg. Sift flour, salt and baking powder. Add alternately with milk. Add vanilla and almond extract. Add cocoa to half the batter. Pour into greased muffin tins, putting in alternate spoons of light and dark batter. Bake in 375° oven for 20 minutes. Serve with 2 tablespoons chocolate sauce on each cup cake.

Lunch and Dinner Menus

MENU 21

Luncheon—230 calories
Chicken Sandwich—180 calories
Tossed Green Salad—45 calories
Coffee with saccharin and skimmed milk—5 calories

Chicken Sandwich

Spread 2 slices of bread with 1 teaspoon diet mayonnaise each. Place 2 slices chicken (3½ inches by 2½ inches by ¼ inch) on one slice, and top with the other slice of bread.

Tossed Green Salad

romaine, escarole, iceberg lettuce—3 leaves each
1 teaspoon salad oil
1 teaspoon vinegar
salt

Break lettuce into bite-size pieces. Sprinkle generously with salt. (This is the secret of a good green salad.) Pour over oil and vinegar and toss well.

Dinner—700 calories
Baked Steak with Mushrooms—310 calories
(4 slices 2 inches by 3 inches by ½ inch)
1 Baked Tomato Stuffed with Cucumber—80 calories
Scalloped Potatoes—115 calories each portion
Custard Meringue Pie—190 calories each portion
Coffee with saccharin and skimmed milk—5 calories

Baked Steak with Mushrooms

steak 2 inches thick (porterhouse or sirloin)
1 tablespoon butter
3 tablespoons Worcestershire sauce
garlic salt, onion salt

85

freshly ground black pepper
1 *can mushrooms*
1 *bouillon cube*

Preheat oven for ½ hour, as hot as possible. Place steak in shallow roasting pan. Sprinkle 1½ tablespoons Worcestershire sauce, liberal amounts of garlic and onion salt and black pepper on meat. Dot with ½ tablespoon butter. Bake for 10 minutes. Turn steak on the other side. Repeat the seasoning. Heap mushrooms on steak, and bake until done as desired, basting mushrooms occasionally with juices in the pan. Heat mushroom liquor. Dissolve bouillon cube in it. Remove steak to serving platter. Combine pan juices with mushroom juice, pour over steak.

Baked Tomato Stuffed with Cucumber (serves four)

4 *medium tomatoes, scooped out and drained*
2 *medium cucumbers, peeled and finely diced*
1 *small onion, grated*
1 *tablespoon butter*
1 *tablespoon lemon juice*
salt, pepper
3 *tablespoons breadcrumbs*

Simmer cucumber, onion, lemon juice, butter and seasonings for 5 minutes. Fill tomatoes with the mixture. Sprinkle with crumbs, and bake in a 425° oven until tomatoes are tender and the crumbs brown.

Scalloped Potatoes (serves four)

3 *potatoes (2 inches by 4 inches)*
1 *medium onion, grated*
1¼ *cups skimmed milk*
1½ *tablespoons flour*
salt, pepper, paprika

Peel and slice potatoes thinly. Put a layer in a greased baking dish. Sprinkle with flour, liberal amounts of seasonings and onion. Repeat. Pour milk over all. Sprinkle top with paprika and bake in a 350° oven for about 1 hour, or until potatoes are tender.

Custard Meringue Pie (serves seven)

Pie Crust—See Lemon Cream Pie (p. 31)

Filling: *3 egg yolks*
⅓ cup sugar
¼ teaspoon salt
2½ tablespoons cornstarch
1 tablespoon butter
2 cups scalded skimmed milk
1 teaspoon vanilla
½ teaspoon nutmeg

Beat egg yolks. Add sugar, salt, cornstarch and butter. Beat well. Add milk gradually. Cook over very low heat, stirring constantly until thick. Add vanilla and nutmeg. Pour into pie shell. Cover with meringue and bake at 300° for 25 to 30 minutes.

Meringue: *2 egg whites*
2 teaspoons water
⅛ teaspoon salt
¼ teaspoon cream of tartar
4 tablespoons sugar
½ teaspoon vanilla

Whip whites, salt and water until foamy. Add cream of tartar. Beat until stiff. Beat in sugar, ½ teaspoon at a time. Fold in vanilla.

MENU 22

LUNCHEON—225 calories
Vegetable Plate with Poached Egg, Anchovy Sauce—
220 calories
Coffee with saccharin and skimmed milk—5 calories

Vegetable Plate with Poached Egg, Anchovy Sauce

1 *large carrot, cut into strips*
½ *cup cooked cauliflower*
8 *asparagus tips*
1 *cooked beet, sliced*
1 *egg*
¼ *tablespoon butter*
1 *teaspoon flour*
¼ *cup skimmed milk*
1 *teaspoon anchovy paste*

Use either fresh or frozen vegetables. If using frozen, follow cooking directions on the package, cooking vegetables separately. (Cut off just what you need. It is not necessary to cook the whole package.) If using fresh vegetables, cook each separately in boiling salted water to cover. Drain well. Arrange vegetables around serving plate. Place poached egg in center. Cover egg with Anchovy Sauce and serve.

Poached Egg—Bring 1 cup salted water to a boil in a shallow pot. Break egg into a saucer. Stir water rapidly. Gently slip egg into the center of the whirlpool. Do not let water boil again. When film forms over the egg and the white is set, remove from water with a perforated spoon.

Anchovy Sauce—Melt butter. Blend in flour. Add hot milk gradually, stirring constantly until thickened. Blend in anchovy paste.

DINNER—680 calories
Shad Roe—350 calories each portion
Sweet and Sour String Beans—85 calories each portion
Parsley Potato—45 calories
Blitzkuchen—195 calories each portion
Coffee with saccharin and skimmed milk—5 calories

Shad Roe (serves four)

> 2 *pairs roe (about 2 pounds)*
> 1 *tablespoon vinegar*
> 2 *teaspoons salt*
> 4 *teaspoons butter, melted*
> *lemon juice*
> *paprika*
> 4 *slices lemon*
> 4 *sprigs watercress*

Parboil roe in water to which 1 tablespoon vinegar and 2 teaspoons salt have been added. Simmer for 12 minutes. Remove roe and cool. Place in greased baking pan. Sprinkle each portion with lemon juice, paprika and ½ teaspoon butter melted. Broil gently until light brown. Turn, repeat seasonings, pour over remaining butter and brown second side. Serve, garnished with lemon slice and watercress.

Sweet and Sour String Beans (serves four)

> 3 *cups cooked string beans (about 1¼ pounds)*
> 1 *tablespoon butter*
> 1½ *tablespoons flour*
> 1 *tablespoon sugar*
> 2 *tablespoons vinegar*

Cook fresh or frozen French-cut beans in boiling salted water. Drain, reserving liquid. Melt butter, blend in flour. Cook, stirring until mixture becomes golden brown. Gradually add hot stock. Continue stirring until sauce thickens. Add sugar and vinegar. Add beans and reheat.

Parsley Potatoes (serves four)

>2 *potatoes (2 inches by 4 inches)*
>4 *teaspoons chopped parsley*

Cut potatoes in half. Cook in boiling salted water to cover until tender. Drain thoroughly. Serve with chopped parsley sprinkled on top.

Blitzkuchen (serves eight)

>½ *cup plus 1 tablespoon sifted cake flour*
>½ *teaspoon baking powder*
>¼ *cup butter*
>½ *cup sugar*
>2 *eggs, separated*
>1 *teaspoon grated lemon rind*
>1 *teaspoon grated orange rind*
>1½ *tablespoons skimmed milk*
>½ *egg white diluted with ½ tablespoon water*
>⅛ *teaspoon salt*
>⅜ *cup sugar*
>1 *tablespoon cinnamon*
>¼ *cup chopped walnuts*

Sift baking powder and flour together. Cream butter. Gradually add sugar, and continue creaming until fluffy. Beat egg yolks well. Add to first mixture with fruit rinds. Add flour gradually, then milk and beat again. Beat egg whites and salt until stiff but not dry. Fold into batter carefully. Pour into greased 8-inch square or 9-inch round pan. Brush with diluted egg white. Mix sugar, nuts and cinnamon. Sprinkle on top. Bake in a 375° oven for about 30 minutes.

Lunch and Dinner Menus

MENU 23

LUNCHEON—235 calories
French Toast with Cinnamon and Sugar—230 calories
Coffee with saccharin and skimmed milk—5 calories

French Toast with Cinnamon and Sugar

2 *slices white bread*
1 *egg*
2 *tablespoons skimmed milk*
1 *teaspoon butter*
1 *teaspoon sugar*
⅓ *teaspoon cinnamon*

Beat egg with milk. Dip bread into mixture, turning on both sides until all the liquid has been absorbed. Grease a heavy iron pan or griddle with the butter. Have the pan well heated. Fry the toast until golden on one side, turn and fry the other side. Serve immediately with mixed sugar and cinnamon sprinkled on top.

DINNER—705 calories
Hungarian Pork Goulash—475 calories each portion
Caraway Potatoes—45 calories each portion
Lemon Snowballs—180 calories each portion
Coffee with saccharin and skimmed milk—5 calories

Hungarian Pork Goulash (serves four)

8 *medium small lean pork chops*
2 *onions*
½ *tablespoon butter*
3 *cups sauerkraut*
1 *teaspoon salt*
½ *tablespoon paprika*

91

1 *cup water*
4 *tablespoons sour cream*

Dice onions fine. Melt butter in a Dutch oven and sauté onions for ½ hour over very low flame. Do not permit them to brown. Trim all excess fat from chops. Add meat, salt and paprika. Cover and allow to simmer for an additional half hour. Add sauerkraut and water, and continue cooking slowly in covered pot for 1 hour. During cooking add additional water if meat and kraut seem dry. Remove from flame, stir in sour cream and serve.

Caraway Potatoes (serves four)

4 *potatoes 2 inches in diameter*
1½ *teaspoons caraway seeds*

Peel potatoes. Boil in salted water to cover. Drain well and serve with caraway seeds sprinkled on top.

Lemon Snowballs (serves four)

1¾ *cups lemon ice*
8 *tablespoons dried cocoanut*

With an ice cream scoop or a spoon, form ice into 4 balls. Roll each ball quickly in two tablespoons of cocoanut.

Lunch and Dinner Menus

MENU 24

LUNCHEON—280 calories
Chopped Chicken and Vegetable Salad—200 calories
Rye Toast with ½ teaspoon butter—75 calories
Coffee with saccharin and skimmed milk—5 calories

Chopped Chicken and Vegetable Salad

3 *slices cold cooked chicken (3½ inches by 2½ inches by ¼ inch)*
¼ *cup cold cooked peas*
¼ *cup cold cooked rice*
½ *stalk celery*
1 *teaspoon chopped pimiento*
1 *tablespoon diet mayonnaise*
salt
lettuce

Dice chicken and celery. Arrange lettuce on serving dish. Blend remaining ingredients together. Add salt to taste. Mound on lettuce.

DINNER—630 calories
Fish Rolls with Lemon Sauce—255 calories each portion
Spinach Soufflé—75 calories each portion
Summer Squash—60 calories each portion
Filled Pancakes—235 calories each portion
Coffee with saccharin and skimmed milk—5 calories

Fish Rolls with Lemon Sauce (serves four)

bones and heads of fish
celery
1 *onion*
8 *slices flounder filet (2 pounds)*

93

16 *large shrimp*
1 *tablespoon butter*
2 *tablespoons flour*
½ *cup skimmed milk*
½ *cup fish stock*
1 *egg yolk*
lemon juice
salt, pepper
dash of cayenne

Place bones and heads of fish, celery and onion in one quart of water. Simmer for ½ hour. Strain, reserving the stock. Peel and de-vein the raw shrimp. Lay two shrimp on top of one end of each filet. Starting at that end, roll fish, so that shrimp will be in the middle. Secure with a toothpick. Simmer fish rolls in stock for 15 minutes. Remove and keep hot. Melt butter, blend in flour. Add ½ cup hot stock and milk gradually, stirring until thickened. Remove from fire. Stir in egg yolk, lemon juice and seasonings to taste. Arrange rolls on platter, and pour sauce over all.

Spinach Soufflé (serves four)

1 *package frozen chopped spinach or*
1½ *cups chopped cooked spinach*
2 *teaspoons butter*
1 *tablespoon flour*
½ *cup spinach water*
½ *teaspoon salt*
½ *teaspoon onion salt*
dash of nutmeg
2 *eggs*

Cook frozen spinach as directed on package. Drain, reserving liquid. With fresh spinach, wash very thoroughly. Put in pot without additional water. Cover and cook about 5 minutes or until tender. Drain well, reserving liquid, and chop. Melt butter in a saucepan. Blend in flour, add spinach water. Stir until thickened. Add nutmeg, salt and onion salt. Mix with spinach. Add egg yolks. Fold in egg whites beaten stiff. Pour into greased casserole. Place in pan of hot water. Bake, covered, at 350° for 30 minutes. Remove pan from water and uncover. Turn heat to 375° and bake for 10 minutes longer.

Summer Squash (serves four)

> 2¾ *pounds yellow summer squash*
> 1½ *tablespoons butter*
> *salt, pepper*

Scrub squash. Slice very thin. (I use a cabbage shredder.) Put in heavy iron pan. Cook, covered, scraping from the bottom every few minutes to prevent sticking. When tender, and slightly brown, in about 20 minutes, add butter and liberal amounts of salt and pepper to taste.

Filled Pancakes (12 pancakes) (serves four)

> 1 *egg*
> ½ *cup flour*
> ½ *cup skimmed milk*
> ½ *cup carbonated water*
> 1 *tablespoon butter*
> ¾ *cup cottage cheese*
> 4 *tablespoons sugar*
> ½ *teaspoon vanilla*
> *rind of* ½ *lemon*
> 1 *teaspoon cinnamon*

Beat egg. Add flour. Beat until smooth. Gradually add milk and then carbonated water, being sure batter remains free of lumps. Let batter stand ½ hour. Heat 7-inch heavy iron frying pan. Grease with a little butter. Pour in scant 2 tablespoons batter, tilting pan to spread it very thin. When pancake is brown on one side, turn and brown the other side. Have a pan or dish over a pot of boiling water. Transfer cooked pancakes to dish to keep warm. To make filling, blend cottage cheese, 2 tablespoons sugar, vanilla and lemon rind. Spread some filling on each pancake and roll. Return filled pancakes to dish over hot water. Place a cover over them and heat through thoroughly for 15 minutes over boiling water. Pancakes and filling must be served hot. Mix remaining 2 tablespoons sugar and cinnamon and sprinkle on rolled pancakes just before serving.

MENU 25

LUNCHEON—205 calories
Cornflakes with Sliced Strawberries—200 calories
Coffee with saccharin and skimmed milk—5 calories

Cornflakes with Strawberries

1 *cup cornflakes*
½ *cup skimmed milk*
½ *cup strawberries*
2 *teaspoons brown sugar*

Pour cereal into a bowl. Put strawberries over cornflakes. Serve with sugar and milk.

DINNER—745 calories
Sweetbreads Supreme—375 calories each portion
Succotash—125 calories each portion
Braised Celery—50 calories each portion
Cinnamon Apple Mousse—185 calories each portion
Coffee with saccharin and skimmed milk—5 calories

Sweetbreads Supreme (serves four)

3 *or* 4 *large veal bones*
1 *quart water*
2½ *pounds sweetbreads*
2 *tablespoons lemon juice*
2 *tablespoons butter*
3 *tablespoons dry sherry*
salt, pepper

Make a veal stock, by cooking the bones in 1 quart of water for 2 hours. Let stock reduce to 1½ cups. Parboil sweetbreads for 20 minutes in water to which lemon juice has been added. Chill. Remove membrane and any hard fibrous matter. Cut sweetbreads into slices $\frac{1}{2}$ inch thick. Sauté sweetbreads in butter in heavy iron pan until light brown. Add hot stock and sherry. Cook rapidly until liquid is reduced by a little more than half, and is thick. Baste constantly. Season to taste with salt and pepper. (Veal cutlet may be substituted for sweetbreads in this recipe.)

Succotash (serves four)

> 1 *cup corn kernels*
> 1 *cup lima beans*
> *salt*
> *freshly ground pepper*

Use either fresh or frozen vegetables. Drain well and combine. Add seasonings to taste.

Braised Celery (serves four)

> 4 *hearts of celery*
> 1$\frac{1}{2}$ *tablespoons butter*
> $\frac{1}{2}$ *cup bouillon*
> *salt, pepper*

Melt butter. Add celery, bouillon and a pinch of salt and pepper. Cover pan and simmer for 20 minutes, or until tender. Uncover. Finish cooking in a 375° oven, basting occasionally until the liquid is absorbed.

Cinnamon Apple Mousse (serves six)

> 6 *medium cooking apples*
> $\frac{1}{4}$ *cup water*
> $\frac{1}{4}$ *pound small red cinnamon candies*
> 1 *teaspoon lemon juice*
> 2 *tablespoons gelatin*
> $\frac{1}{2}$ *cup cold water*
> $\frac{1}{2}$ *cup boiling water*
> 1 *tablespoon granulated sugar*

Cut cored, unpeeled apples into slices $\frac{1}{2}$ inch thick. Cook, covered, with $\frac{1}{4}$ cup water, candies and lemon juice until very tender. Mash through a sieve. Sprinkle gelatin on remaining cold water to soften, then dissolve in boiling water. Mix with apple pulp. Lightly oil a mold, sprinkle with sugar and pour mixture into it. Chill until firm. This is better done early in the morning. Unmold just before serving.

MENU 26

LUNCHEON—220 calories
Baked Oysters—120 calories
Sliced Tomato—20 calories
Rye Toast with ½ teaspoon butter—75 calories
Coffee with saccharin and skimmed milk—5 calories

Baked Oysters

> 6 *oysters on the half shell*
> 3 *slices bacon*
> 2 *teaspoons chopped parsley*
> *Worcestershire sauce*
> *lemon juice*

Fry bacon very well. Drain and dry on absorbent paper. Crumble. Place oysters on a pie plate. Sprinkle with parsley and bacon. Put a few drops of Worcestershire sauce and lemon juice on each. Put in a 400° oven, and bake for about 8 minutes, or until plump.

DINNER—735 calories
Veal Meatballs in Dill Sauce—350 calories each portion
¾ cup Diet Spaghetti—35 calories
Artichoke with Drawn Butter—125 calories
Blueberry Pie—220 calories each portion
Coffee with saccharin and skimmed milk—5 calories

Veal Meatballs in Dill Sauce (serves four)

> 1¼ *pounds boneless veal*
> ½ *cup breadcrumbs*
> 1 *egg*
> ½ *teaspoon nutmeg*
> 1 *teaspoon salt*

⅛ teaspoon white pepper
2 cups bouillon
⅓ pound mushrooms
1 teaspoon butter
2 tablespoons flour
½ cup skimmed milk
2 tablespoons chopped fresh dill
paprika

Have the veal ground very fine. Mix with the breadcrumbs, ¼ cup bouillon, the egg yolk, salt, pepper and nutmeg. Fold in the egg white beaten stiff. Handling gently, form into balls 1 inch in diameter. Simmer in the remaining bouillon for ½ hour. Slice the mushrooms thin. Sauté in butter in a heavy iron pan for 3 minutes. Sprinkle flour over mushrooms, stirring constantly. Add 1 cup of bouillon in which meatballs have cooked and hot skimmed milk to pan very gradually, stirring all the while. Cook until thickened. Add dill, a dash of paprika and more salt to taste. Remove meatballs to serving platter. Pour sauce over cooked meat and serve.

Diet Spaghetti

Diet spaghetti is cooked just as ordinary spaghetti in an abundance of boiling salted water. The only difference is that it will take a few more minutes to become tender. Allow about 15 to 18 minutes.

Artichoke with Drawn Butter (serves four)

Cook 4 artichokes as on page 80, but serve hot. To make drawn butter, place 2 tablespoons butter in dish over pan of hot water or top of double boiler. Allow to melt over boiling water. Serve artichoke on a salad plate with melted butter in individual sauce dishes.

Blueberry Pie (serves eight)

    Pie Crust—See Glazed Strawberry Tart, page 29

    4 *cups blueberries*

    ½ *cup sugar*

    2 *tablespoons flour*

    ½ *teaspoon cinnamon*

Prepare piecrust as for Glazed Strawberry Tart, but do not bake. Combine remaining ingredients. Pour into unbaked crust. Bake in a 375° oven for three-quarters of an hour.

Note: Frozen or canned berries may be used. In both cases, drain off all the juice and decrease the amount of sugar. I find that when I use these berries, they are sufficiently sweet not to need any additional sugar.

MENU 27

LUNCHEON—215 calories
Smoked Salmon and Chive Cheese Sandwich—210 calories
Coffee with saccharin and skimmed milk—5 calories

Smoked Salmon and Chive Cheese Sandwich

2 *slices low-calorie brown bread*
1 *ounce smoked salmon*
½ *tablespoon chive cheese*
lettuce

Spread 1 slice of bread with cheese. Place salmon over cheese. Cover with lettuce, and top with the other slice of bread.

DINNER—715 calories
Calves Liver and Veal Kidney Flambé—350 calories each portion
¾ cup Parslied Rice—120 calories
Hearts of Lettuce, Tomato and Endive Salad —50 calories each portion
Orange Tapioca Shells—190 calories each portion
Coffee with saccharin and skimmed milk—5 calories

Calves Liver and Veal Kidney Flambé (serves four)

½ *pound calves liver*
1 *pound veal kidney*
1 *small onion*
½ *pound mushrooms*
jigger of brandy
2 *tablespoons butter*
3 *tablespoons flour*
½ *cup skimmed milk*
1 *cup bouillon*

1 *teaspoon dry mustard*
salt, pepper

Trim off the skin and excess fat from the kidneys. Cut into slices ¼ inch thick. Cut liver into julienne strips. Slice mushrooms. Dice onion. Melt butter in heavy iron frying pan. Add liver, kidneys, mushrooms and onion. Sauté for about 5 minutes or until meats are brown. Pour brandy in pan and light. Let flame burn out by itself. Sprinkle flour over mixture, blending with juices. Gradually add hot milk and bouillon, stirring constantly until mixture thickens. Add mustard and salt and pepper to taste.

Parsleyed Rice

See Page 80 for cooking directions. For each portion on this menu of ¾ cup of cooked rice, allow 3 tablespoons of raw. To each serving, add 1½ teaspoons chopped parsley and mix lightly with rice.

Hearts of Lettuce, Tomato and Endive Salad (serves four)

medium head lettuce
2 *large tomatoes*
20 *pieces endive (approx. one medium head)*
1 *tablespoon chili sauce*
1 *tablespoon diet mayonnaise*
1 *tablespoon skimmed milk*

Cut lettuce into 4 equal wedges. Slice tomatoes. Arrange lettuce, tomatoes and endive on individual salad plates. Mix chili sauce, mayonnaise and milk. Pour dressing over salad.

Orange Tapioca Shells (serves four)

2 *large oranges*
1 *package prepared orange tapioca mix*
2 *cups skimmed milk*

Prepare pudding according to directions on the package. Pour into a bowl, place a piece of waxed paper directly on the pudding to prevent the formation of a skin on top. Chill. Shortly before serving, cut oranges in half crosswise. Carefully remove meat and reserve. With a sharp knife scrape shells clean. Fill each with ½ cup of pudding. Arrange orange segments on top.

The following four menus were devised with two thoughts in mind. So many youngsters, though they eat and relish all the dishes on the preceding pages, do occasionally want to enjoy typical teen-age fare. Here I've included the hamburgers, the frankfurters and the ice cream cones that they always incorporate when they plan a party menu. There's no reason why the same food shouldn't take its place right on the diet. Then, I've tried to make suggestions for the school-lunch problem, with a sandwich most often the only possible answer. Though I've specified low-calorie brown bread, I do so only because Jill likes its taste and feels that she has the largest bulk with the lowest number of calories. You may substitute any other bread you prefer. You may also use any of the preceding luncheon salads or cold meats, packed in paper containers, to break the monotony of the daily sandwich. As I have said before, though, Jill did not want to appear conspicuous among her friends by eating differently. I deferred to her wishes just, as with Jill as a yardstick, I tried in the following menus to consider chiefly the teen-age palate.

MENU 28

LUNCHEON—235 calories
Salmon Salad Sandwich—155 calories
Cucumber Wedges—30 calories
Fresh Pear—50 calories

Salmon Salad Sandwich

2 slices low-calorie brown bread
¼ cup canned salmon
½ stalk celery
lettuce
lemon juice
freshly ground black pepper

Dice celery. Flake salmon. Mix with the celery and pepper and lemon juice to taste. Spread on one slice of bread, top with a lettuce leaf and the other slice of bread.

Cucumber Wedges

Peel cucumber. Slice into 4 lengthwise pieces. Season with salt and pepper.

MIDAFTERNOON CHOCOLATE MILKSHAKE—75 calories

Combine 6 ounces of skimmed milk and 1 teaspoon of diet chocolate sauce in an electric blender or bowl. Beat until frothy.

DINNER—625 calories
2 Lamb Chops (1 inch thick)—265 calories
Fresh Peas—55 calories
Romaine and Watercress Salad, Russian Dressing—30 calories
Banana Split—205 calories
6 ounces Skimmed Milk—70 calories

Lamb Chops

Rub chops with a cut clove of garlic (optional). Place about 1 inch from broiler flame. Broil for 4 minutes, season with salt and pepper. Turn on other side, broil until cooked as desired and repeat seasoning.

Fresh Peas

Allow ½ cup fresh or frozen peas for each portion. Cook until just tender in boiling water, to which 1 teaspoon sugar has been added. Drain well.

Romaine and Watercress Salad, Russian Dressing (serves four)

> 20 *leaves romaine lettuce (approx. 1 medium head)*
> 40 *pieces watercress (approx. 1 large bunch)*
> 4 *teaspoons chili sauce*
> 4 *teaspoons diet mayonnaise*
> 1 *teaspoon chopped chives*
> *few drops lemon juice*
> *salt*

Make a bed of the romaine lettuce in a salad bowl. Sprinkle with salt. Heap watercress in the center. Make a dressing of the chili sauce, mayonnaise, chives and lemon juice to taste. Pour over all.

Banana Split (serves four)

> 2 *bananas*
> 1 *cup vanilla ice cream*
> 4 *tablespoons whipped cream, scant*
> 8 *pecan halves, chopped*
> 4 *maraschino cherries*

Cut bananas in half, crosswise. Cut each half into 4 lengthwise strips. Arrange pieces in individual serving dishes. Place a scoop of ice cream in the center. Top with cream, chopped nuts and a cherry.

MENU 29

LUNCHEON—230 calories
Cream Cheese and Relish Sandwich—170 calories
2 large Stalks Celery—10 calories
1 medium Orange—50 calories

Cream Cheese and Relish Sandwich

2 *slices low-calorie brown bread*
1 *tablespoon cream cheese*
1 *teaspoon India relish*
1 *teaspoon diet mayonnaise*
lettuce

Blend cheese and relish. Spread on one slice of bread. Cover with lettuce and the other slice of bread which has been spread with the mayonnaise.

MIDAFTERNOON CHOCOLATE MILKSHAKE—75 calories

DINNER—625 calories
De Luxe Chicken Chow Mein—300 calories each portion
1 cup Pan Fried Noodles—55 calories
Swedish Baked Apple—200 calories
6 ounces Skimmed Milk—70 calories

De Luxe Chicken Chow Mein (serves four)

4-*pound fowl*
2 *onions*
2 *stalks celery*
2 *carrots*
4 *peppercorns*
salt
½ *tablespoon butter*

1 *onion, diced*
4 *stalks celery, cut in julienne strips*
¾ *pound mushrooms, sliced*
1 *cup bean sprouts*
1 *cup water chestnuts, thinly sliced*
1 *cup bamboo shoots*
1½ *tablespoons cornstarch*
3 *tablespoons soy sauce*

Put chicken, 2 onions, 2 stalks celery, carrots, peppercorns in a pot with boiling salted water to cover. Cover and simmer gently until tender, about 2 hours. Skin chicken, remove meat from bones and cut into bite-size pieces. Strain broth and continue cooking, uncovered, until 1½ cups remain. Reserve. In a heavy iron pan, melt butter. Cook onion until golden. Add mushrooms and celery strips. Cook 3 minutes. Add bean sprouts, chestnuts and bamboo shoots. Blend corn starch, soy sauce and remaining broth. Gradually add to the pan, stirring constantly until thickened. (Add more soy sauce, if desired.) Add chicken. Heat thoroughly, stirring all the while.

Pan Fried Noodles (serves four)

4 *cups cooked diet noodles, chilled*
2 *teaspoons butter*

Melt butter in heavy iron frying pan. Add noodles. Fry, stirring constantly, until browned.

Swedish Baked Apple (serves four)

4 *baking apples*
20 *almonds*
2 *tablespoons brown sugar*
1 *tablespoon water*
2 *teaspoons melted butter*
1 *tablespoon brown sugar*

¼ *cup breadcrumbs*
½ *teaspoon cinnamon*

Grind almonds. Mix with water and 2 tablespoons sugar until smooth. Peel and core apples. Fill centers with almond paste. Brush apples with butter. Mix cinnamon, 1 tablespoon sugar and breadcrumbs. Roll apples in this mixture. Place in greased baking dish. Bake at 425° for 25 minutes, or until soft.

Lunch and Dinner Menus

MENU 30

<small>Luncheon—205 calories</small>
Lettuce and Tomato Sandwich—135 calories
Carrot Strips—30 calories
2 Apricots—40 calories

Lettuce and Tomato Sandwich

2 *slices low-calorie brown bread*
1 *medium tomato sliced*
1 *teaspoon diet mayonnaise*
lettuce

Spread mayonnaise on bread. Arrange tomato slices on top, sprinkle with salt, cover with lettuce and top with other slice of bread.

Carrot Strips

Cut one large carrot into julienne strips. Chill.

Midafternoon Chocolate Milkshake—75 calories

Dinner—660 calories
Grilled Hamburgers with Barbecue Sauce—365 calories each portion
Potato Parmesan—65 calories each portion
⅔ cup Brussels Sprouts—15 calories
Chocolate Pear Supreme—145 calories each portion
6 ounces Skimmed Milk—70 calories

Grilled Hamburgers with Barbecue Sauce (serves four)

2 *pounds chopped lean beef*
2 *teaspoons prepared mustard*
2 *teaspoons soy sauce*
salt, pepper

111

1 tablespoon butter
1 tablespon flour
½ teaspoon prepared mustard
1 tablespoon chili sauce
½ teaspoon Worcestershire sauce
1 tablespoon vinegar
½ teaspoon brown sugar
¼ teaspoon salt
½ cup boiling water

Combine meat, 2 teaspoons mustard, soy sauce and salt and pepper to taste. Shape into 8 patties. Either broil under broiler or pan-broil by preheating heavy iron frying pan, sprinkling the pan with salt, and cooking hamburgers until done as desired. To make the sauce, melt the butter. Blend in flour, mustard, chili sauce, Worcestershire sauce, vinegar, brown sugar and salt. Gradually add water, stirring constantly until thickened.

Potato Parmesan (serves four)

2 potatoes (2 inches by 4 inches)
½ cup skimmed milk
2 tablespoons grated Parmesan cheese
salt, pepper

Cook potatoes in boiling salted water to cover until tender. Drain well. Put through ricer. Add hot milk, cheese and salt and pepper to taste. Whip until light and fluffy.

Brussels Sprouts

Use frozen or fresh vegetable. Cook frozen vegetable as directed on package. Soak fresh sprouts in salted water for 15 minutes. Cook in boiling salted water to cover until tender.

Chocolate Pear Supreme (serves four)

4 *whole canned pears*
4 *tablespoons diet chocolate sauce*
1 *egg white*
⅓ *cup sugar*
¼ *teaspoon vanilla*
pinch salt

Beat egg white until stiff. Add sugar, 1 teaspoon at a time, beating continually. Add salt and vanilla. Divide into 4 oval mounds on a greased baking sheet. Make a slight depression in the center of each with the back of a spoon. Bake at 275° for 18 minutes. Turn off heat. Leave meringues in oven 1 hour to dry out. To serve, place one meringue shell on each plate, top with a well-drained pear, and cover with chocolate sauce.

MENU 31

Luncheon—270 calories

Egg Salad Sandwich—185 calories
1 Medium Tomato—20 calories
1 Medium Apple—65 calories

Egg Salad Sandwich

> 2 *slices low-calorie brown bread*
> 1 *egg*
> 1½ *teaspoons diet mayonnaise*
> *lettuce*
> *salt, pepper*

Hard boil egg. Peel and put through ricer. Mix with mayonnaise and salt and pepper to taste. Spread on one slice of bread, cover with lettuce and top with other slice of bread.

Midafternoon Chocolate Milkshake—75 calories

Dinner—600 calories

Grilled Frankfurters with Piquant Mustard—
220 calories each portion
German Potato Salad—70 calories each portion
Iced Relish Bowl—40 calories each portion
Vanilla Ice Cream Cone—200 calories
6 Ounces Skimmed Milk—70 calories

Grilled Frankfurters with Piquant Mustard (serves four)

> 8 *beef frankfurters*
> 1 *tablespoon diet mayonnaise*
> 2 *teaspoons prepared mustard*
> 2 *teaspoons India relish*

Parboil frankfurters for 4 minutes. Grill in a heavy iron frying pan, turning until brown on all sides. Combine mustard, mayonnaise and relish. Serve dressing on the side.

German Potato Salad (serves four)

2 *potatoes (2 inches by 4 inches)*
½ *egg*
1½ *teaspoons butter, melted*
¼ *cup vinegar*
2 *tablespoons water*
½ *small onion, grated*
½ *teaspoon celery seed*
salt, pepper

Pare potatoes. Cook in boiling salted water to cover until tender. Slice. Beat one whole egg until light. Put half the beaten egg in a small bowl. Add butter, hot vinegar, hot water, onion, celery seed, salt and pepper. Pour over hot sliced potatoes and blend. This salad is equally good served hot or cool, but never chilled.

Iced Relish Bowl (serves four)

8 *radishes*
4 *green olives*
4 *ripe olives*
4 *large stalks celery*
2 *large carrots*

Cut radishes into roses. With a small sharp knife snip off a little of the radish top. Then, working from that end, cut just under skin toward the bottom of the radish, to form 4 petals around it. Cut each piece of celery into three, crosswise. Fringe each end, by making 4 or 5 ½-inch incisions. Cut carrots into thin lengthwise strips. Put all vegetables in ice water in refrigerator. When ready to serve, fill a large bowl with cracked ice. Arrange vegetables and olives on bed of ice.

Vanilla Ice Cream Cone

Allow ¼ cup of ice cream to each cone. Top each cone with ½ teaspoon chocolate sprinkles.

DRIVE SLOW
SCHOOL ZONE

SCHOOL ZONE

menu
Shrimp
Lettuce
Bread

SUGGESTIONS FOR SCHOOL LUNCHES

MENU
SCHOOL LUNCHES

6. Suggestions for School Lunches

School Lunches Can Be Varied:

SCHOOL LUNCH 1—235 calories

Ripe Olive and Celery Sandwich—155 calories

⅔ cup Raw Cauliflower—30 calories

½ cup Fresh Cherries—50 calories

Ripe Olive and Celery Sandwich

2 *slices low-calorie brown bread*

4 *ripe olives*

1 *stalk celery*

1 *teaspoon diet mayonnaise*

lettuce

Cut celery into very fine dice. Mince olives. Combine vegetables. Blend with mayonnaise. Spread on one slice of bread, cover with lettuce and top with other slice of bread.

SCHOOL LUNCH 2—250 calories

Shrimp and Chopped Chive Sandwich—155 calories

2 large Stalks Celery—10 calories

Medium Banana—85 calories

119

Shrimp and Chopped Chive Sandwich

> 2 *slices low-calorie brown bread*
> $\frac{1}{4}$ *cup cooked and cleaned shrimp*
> $\frac{1}{2}$ *teaspoon chopped chives*
> 1 *teaspoon diet mayonnaise*
> 1 *teaspoon chili sauce*
> *lettuce*

Dice shrimp. Blend mayonnaise, chili sauce and chives. Combine with shrimps. Spread mixture on one slice of bread, cover with lettuce and top with other slice of bread.

SCHOOL LUNCH 3—235 calories

Diced Bacon and Celery Sandwich—165 calories

Cucumber Slices—30 calories

$\frac{1}{2}$ cup Fresh Blueberries—40 calories

Diced Bacon and Celery Sandwich

> 2 *slices low-calorie brown bread*
> 2 *slices lean bacon*
> $\frac{1}{2}$ *stalk celery*
> 1 *teaspoon diet mayonnaise*
> *lettuce*

Fry bacon until crisp. Drain thoroughly on absorbent paper. Crumble. Cut celery into fine dice. Mix with bacon and mayonnaise. Spread on one slice of bread, cover with lettuce and top with other slice of bread.

Note: Fresh berries or sliced fruits such as melon or pineapple may very satisfactorily be carried to school packed in sandwich bags.

SCHOOL LUNCH 4—235 calories

Cottage Cheese and Raw Vegetable Sandwich—140 calories

Medium Tomato—20 calories

3 Prunes—75 calories

Suggestions for School Lunches

Cottage Cheese and Raw Vegetable Sandwich

  2 *slices low-calorie brown bread*
  2 *tablespoons cottage cheese*
  2 *tablespoons raw peas*
  2 *tablespoons grated carrot*
  ¼ *teaspoon onion salt*

Combine cheese, vegetables and seasonings. Spread on one slice of bread and top with the other.

SCHOOL LUNCH 5—240 calories
Chopped Liver and Relish Sandwich—155 calories
Carrot Strips—30 calories
2 Plums—55 calories

Chopped Liver and Relish Sandwich

  2 *slices low-calorie brown bread*
  Calves liver (1½ inches by 1½ inches by ½ inch)
  ⅓ *teaspoon butter*
  1 *teaspoon diet mayonnaise*
  1 *teaspoon India relish*
  lettuce

Sauté liver quickly in butter. Chop very fine. Mix with relish and mayonnaise. Spread on one slice of bread, cover with lettuce and top with the other slice of bread.

SCHOOL LUNCH 6—230 calories
Diced Tongue and Cole Slaw Sandwich—175 calories
2 large Stalks Celery—10 calories
1 Slice Pineapple—45 calories

Diced Tongue and Cole Slaw Sandwich

  2 *slices low-calorie brown bread*
  1 *ounce of cooked tongue*

121

¼ *cup finely chopped cabbage*
1 *teaspoon diet mayonnaise*
1 *teaspoon chili sauce*

Cut tongue into fine dice. Blend mayonnaise and chili sauce. Mix with cabbage and tongue. Place on one slice of bread and cover with the other.

SCHOOL LUNCH 7—215 calories
Chopped Chicken and Vegetable Sandwich—155 calories
Cucumber Slices—30 calories
½ cup Fresh Strawberries—30 calories

Chopped Chicken and Vegetable Sandwich

2 *slices low-calorie brown bread*
1 *slice chicken (3½ inches by 2½ inches by ¼ inch)*
¼ *carrot*
1 *teaspoon chopped parsley*
1 *teaspoon diet mayonnaise*
1 *teaspoon chili sauce*
pinch salt
lettuce

Mince chicken and carrot. Blend mayonnaise and chili sauce. Combine with chicken, carrot and parsley. Add salt to taste. Spread on one slice of bread, cover with lettuce and top with the other slice of bread.

SCHOOL LUNCH 8—210 calories
Roast Veal and Dill Pickle Sandwich—165 calories
⅔ cup Raw Cauliflower—30 calories
¼ medium Cantaloupe, peeled and sliced—25 calories

Roast Veal and Dill Pickle Sandwich

2 *slices low-calorie brown bread*
1 *slice roast veal (4½ inches by 2¾ inches by ⅛ inch)*

Suggestions for School Lunches

¼ *large dill pickle*
½ *teaspoon diet mayonnaise*
lettuce

Spread one slice of bread with mayonnaise. Place veal on bread. Cover with thin slices of pickle and lettuce and top with the other slice of bread.

SCHOOL LUNCH 9—240 calories
Sliced Egg and Watercress Sandwich—185 calories
Medium Tomato—20 calories
Medium Tangerine—35 calories

Sliced Egg and Watercress Sandwich

2 *slices low-calorie brown bread*
1 *hard-boiled egg*
6 *pieces watercress*
½ *teaspoon prepared mustard*
½ *teaspoon diet mayonnaise*
salt

Slice egg. Blend mustard and mayonnaise and spread on one slice of bread. Arrange egg on bread, sprinkle lightly with salt, cover with cress and top with the other slice of bread.

SCHOOL LUNCH 10—240 calories
Boston Brown Bread and Cream Cheese—175 calories
Carrot Strips—30 calories
½ cup Fresh Blackberries—35 calories

Boston Brown Bread and Cream Cheese

3 *slices Boston Brown Bread (3 inches diameter ¼ inch thick)*
1½ *tablespoons cream cheese*

Cut one piece of bread in half. Spread cheese on 1½ slices of bread and top with the remaining slices.

123

Reduce and Enjoy It Cookbook

SCHOOL LUNCH 11—215 calories
Scrambled Egg and Chive Sandwich—180 calories
2 large Stalks Celery—10 calories
⅛ medium Honeydew Melon, peeled and sliced—25 calories

Scrambled Egg and Chive Sandwich

2 *slices low-calorie brown bread*
1 *egg*
¼ *teaspoon butter*
1 *teaspoon chopped chives*
salt, pepper

Heat heavy iron skillet. Beat egg, salt and pepper, with a fork. Melt butter in skillet. Turn down flame and pour in egg. Stir constantly until cooked. Heap on one slice of bread, sprinkle with chives and cover with the other slice of bread.

Note: When cooking eggs with very little butter, always preheat the pan. This prevents sticking. While cooking, however, the flame should be very low.

SCHOOL LUNCH 12—230 calories
Tuna Fish Salad Sandwich—160 calories
Medium Tomato—20 calories
2 Sickle Pears—50 calories

Tuna Fish Salad Sandwich

2 *slices low-calorie brown bread*
¼ *cup tuna fish*
½ *stalk celery*
1 *teaspoon diet mayonnaise*
lemon juice
lettuce

Drain fish very well. Flake fish, and cut celery into fine dice. Mix celery, fish and mayonnaise. Add lemon juice to taste.

124

Suggestions for School Lunches

Spread on one slice of bread, cover with lettuce and top with the other slice of bread.

SCHOOL LUNCH 13—240 calories
Chicken Sandwich with Curry Mayonnaise—145 calories
Cucumber Slices—30 calories
2 Lady Apples—65 calories

Chicken Sandwich with Curry Mayonnaise

> 2 *slices low-calorie brown bread*
> 1 *slice chicken (3½ inches by 2½ inches by ¼ inch)*
> 1 *teaspoon diet mayonnaise*
> *pinch curry powder*
> *lettuce*

Flavor mayonnaise with curry powder. Spread on bread. Place chicken on one slice, cover with lettuce and top with the other slice of bread.

SCHOOL LUNCH 14—230 calories
Roquefort Cheese and Tomato Sandwich—170 calories
2 large Stalks Celery—10 calories
½ slice Watermelon—50 calories (6 inches diameter, ¾ inch thick)

Roquefort Cheese and Tomato Sandwich

> 2 *slices low-calorie brown bread*
> *Roquefort cheese (½ packaged triangle)*
> 1½ *teaspoons skimmed milk*
> *medium tomato*
> 1 *teaspoon diet mayonnaise*

Mash cheese and blend with milk until of smooth consistency. Spread on one slice of bread, cover with sliced tomato and top with the other slice of bread, which has been spread with the mayonnaise.

125

SCHOOL LUNCH 15—245 calories
Cottage Cheese and Jelly Sandwich—165 calories
Carrot Sticks—30 calories
Large Green Gage Plum—50 calories

Cottage Cheese and Jelly Sandwich

> 2 *slices low-calorie brown bread*
> 2 *tablespoons cottage cheese*
> 2 *teaspoons jelly*

Spread cheese on one slice of bread. Cover with jelly and top with the other slice of bread.

SCHOOL LUNCH 16—230 calories
Chopped Chicken Giblet and Celery Sandwich—150 calories
⅔ cup Raw Cauliflower—30 calories
Nectarine—50 calories

Chopped Chicken Giblet and Celery Sandwich

> 2 *slices low-calorie brown bread*
> 1 *chicken giblet, boiled*
> ½ *stalk celery*
> 1½ *teaspoons diet mayonnaise*
> *pinch salt*
> *lettuce*

Mince giblet. Dice celery. Mix mayonnaise with celery and meat. Season with salt. Spread on one slice of bread. Cover with lettuce and top with the other slice of bread.

CALORIC

INDEX

Caloric Index

Alcoholic Beverages		
Beer, lager	8 ounces	125
Bourbon	1 jigger	100
Brandy	1 jigger	100
Cordials	cordial glass	80-100
Gin	jigger	75
Rum, Bacardi	jigger	75
Rye	jigger	150
Scotch	jigger	85
Sherry	2 ounces	85
Wine, Red table	3.2 ounces	75
Wine, White table	3.2 ounces	75
Alligator pear	$\frac{1}{2}$ small	155
Almonds	10	65
Almonds, salted	10	100
Angel Cake	$1\frac{1}{4}''$ x $2''$ x $2\frac{1}{2}''$	100
Apple	1 large	100
Apple	1 medium	65
Apple pie (9")	$\frac{1}{6}$ of pie	300
Applesauce	$\frac{1}{3}$ cup	100
Apricot, canned drained	1	25

Apricot, fresh	1	20
Artichoke	1	75
Asparagus tips, canned	5	15
Asparagus, fresh	8, 4″ long	20
Asparagus soup, creamed	½ cup	100
Bacon	4 slices, crisp, drained	100
Bamboo shoots	¾ cup	25
Banana	1 medium	85
Bass	3½ ounces	85
Beans, baked	⅓ cup	100
Beans, lima, fresh, cooked	½ cup	100
Bean sprouts	1 cup	30
Beans, string, cooked	1 cup	40
Beef, corned, lean	4½″ x 2½″ x ⅛″	50
Beef, ground, lean	¼ pound	170
Beef, roast, lean	4½″ x 2½″ x ½″	165
Beef, steak, lean, broiled	2″ x 3″ x 1″	120
Beef liver	4″ x 3″ x ½″	100
Beets	⅓ cup	25
Blackberries	½ cup	35
Blueberries	⅔ cup	50
Blueberry pie	⅙ of a pie	340
Bluefish	3½ ounces	90
Bouillon	1 cup	25
Bread, Boston brown	3″ diameter ⅜″ thick	50
Bread, rye	3½″ x 4″ x ⅜″	55
Bread, white	3″ x 3½″ x ½″	50
Bread, whole-wheat	3¾″ x 3″ x ½″	65
Bread crumbs	1 cup	400
Bread sticks, diet	1	5
Broccoli, steamed	2⅓ cup	100
Brussels sprouts, cooked	⅔ cup	15
Butter	1 tablespoon	100
Buttermilk	½ cup scant	40

Cabbage, cooked	⅔ cup	30
Cabbage, shredded	½ cup	10
Candy, hard	1 ounce	100
Cantaloupe	1-5″ diameter	100
Carrot	1 large	30
Cauliflower, cooked	1 cup	30
Cauliflower, raw	⅔ cup	30
Celery	1 stalk	5
Celery root	⅓ cup	25
Celery soup, cream of	½ cup	100
Cheese, American	1 packaged slice	100
Cheese, American grated	1 cup	500
Cheese, Camembert	1 ounce	85
Cheese, cottage	5 tablespoons	55
Cheese, cream or chive	1 tablespoon	50
Cheese, Parmesan grated	2 tablespoons	35
Cheese, Roquefort	1 triangle package (¾ oz.)	75
Cherries, canned, drained	1 cup	125
Cherries, fresh	1 cup	100
Chestnuts	7	100
Chicken, broiler	½ medium	110
Chicken, lean, cooked	3 slices—3½″ x 2½″ x ¼″	100
Chicken giblet	1 ounce	35
Chicken liver	1 1-ounce	40
Chili sauce	1 tablespoon	25
Chocolate, candy bar, plain	1 ounce	240
Chocolate, candy bar, with almonds	1 ounce	200
Chocolate, sweet milk	2¼″ x 1″ x ¼″	100
Chocolate, unsweetened	1 square	175
Chocolate loaf cake	2½″ x 2½″ x ⅞″	100
Chocolate sauce, diet	1 tablespoon	15
Chocolate syrup	1 tablespoon	50
Clams, cherrystone	6	75
Coca Cola	1 bottle	100

Cocoa	1 tablespoon	35
Coconut, dried	½ cup	275
Codfish	3½ ounces	85
Coffee	1 cup	0
Coffeecake	3″ x 2″ x ¾″	175
Corn	1 ear, 6″ long	70
Corn, canned	⅓ cup	100
Cornflakes	½ cup	50
Cornmeal	1 tablespoon	35
Cornstarch	1 tablespoon	35
Corn syrup	1⅓ tablespoons	100
Crabmeat	½ cup	65
Cracker, graham	1	35
Cracker, saltine	1	15
Cracker, Uneeda	1	25
Cranberries	1 cup	50
Cranberry sauce	¼ cup scant	100
Cream, heavy	2 tablespoons or 3½ tablespoons whipped	115
Cream, light	1 tablespoon	30
Cream, sour	1 tablespoon	35
Cucumber	1 medium	30
Currants, dried	1 cup	500
Currants, fresh	1 cup	65
Custard	⅓ cup	100
Custard pie	⅙ of a pie	200
Dates	1	25
Doughnuts, plain	1	200
Duck, raw	1¾″ x 1″ x ¼″	75
Egg	1	70
Egg white	1	10
Egg yolk	1	60
Eggplant	4½″ diameter x ½″ thick	20
Endive	10 stalks	15

Caloric Index

Farina	1 tablespoon	25
Fats	1 tablespoon	100
Figs, dried	2 small	105
Figs, fresh	1 large, or 2 small	50
Filberts	10	70
Flounder	$3\frac{1}{2}$ ounces	65
Flour, white	1 tablespoon	25
Flour, white	1 cup	450
Frankfurter	$4\frac{1}{4}''$ long	75
French dressing, diet, bottled	4 tablespoons	$\frac{1}{2}$
Gelatin, granulated	1 tablespoon	25
Gingerale	1 cup	65
Gingerbread	$1'' \times 2'' \times 2''$	100
Gingersnap	$1\frac{3}{4}''$ diameter	15
Goose, raw	$3'' \times 3'' \times \frac{1}{8}''$	115
Grapefruit	$\frac{1}{2}$ medium	35
Grapefruit juice	$\frac{1}{2}$ cup scant	40
Grape juice	$\frac{1}{2}$ cup scant	60
Grapenuts	$\frac{1}{2}$ cup scant	180
Grapes, Concord	24	80
Grapes, Malaga	12	45
Griddlecakes	$4\frac{1}{2}''$ diameter	100
Gumdrops	25 very small	100
Haddock, raw	$3\frac{1}{2}$ ounces	70
Halibut, raw	$3\frac{1}{2}$ ounces	120
Ham, lean, boiled	$4'' \times 4'' \times \frac{1}{8}''$	70
Ham, lean, fresh, raw	$2\frac{1}{4}'' \times 1\frac{1}{2}'' \times \frac{1}{8}''$	115
Ham, lean, smoked, raw	$4\frac{1}{2}'' \times 4\frac{1}{2}'' \times \frac{1}{8}''$	80
Herring, pickled	2 small	115
Hickory nuts	12-15	100
Honey	1 tablespoon	100
Honeydew melon	$\frac{1}{8}$ medium	25
Horseradish	5 teaspoons	10
Huckleberries	$\frac{2}{3}$ cup	65

Ice cream, commercial	¼ cup	100
Jello	1 box	340
Jelly	1¾ tablespoons	100
Jelly beans	15	100
Junket	⅜ cup	100
Kale, cooked	1 cup	35
Kohlrabi, fresh	⅔ cup	30
Lady fingers	1 small	25
Lamb, roast leg	4½″ x 2″ x ⅛″	50
Lamb chops, lean	2″ x 1½″ x ¾″	100
Lard	1 tablespoon scant	100
Leeks	5 inches long	15
Lemon	1 medium	25
Lemon ice	½ cup scant	100
Lemon juice	1 tablespoon	5
Lettuce	10 leaves or ¼ small head	10
Lobster	1 medium or ⅔ cup meat	100
Macaroni, boiled	¾ cup	90
Macaroons	1	50
Mackerel, raw	3½ ounces	140
Maple syrup	1 tablespoon	65
Marshmallows	1¼″ diameter	20
Mayonnaise	1 tablespoon	100
Mayonnaise, diet, commercial	1 tablespoon	25
Milk, condensed, sweetened	1 tablespoon	50
Milk, evaporated, unsweetened	1 tablespoon	20
Milk, skimmed	1 cup	90
Milk, whole	1 cup	170
Molasses	1 tablespoon	65
Muffin, bran	2¾″ diameter	115
Muffin, corn	2¾″ diameter	135

Muffin, one egg	2¾″ diameter	130
Mushrooms	12 medium or ¼ pound	50
Mustard, prepared	1 teaspoon	10
Nabisco	1	20
Nectarine	1	50
Noodles, cooked	¾ cup	90
Noodles, diet, cooked	¾ cup	30
Oatmeal	⅓ cup scant	80
Okra	½ cup	25
Oleomargarine	1 tablespoon	100
Olive oil	1 tablespoon	100
Olives, green	12-16 medium	100
Olives, ripe	8-10 medium	100
Onion	1 small	10
Orange	1 medium	50
Orange ice	⅜ cup	100
Orange juice	½ cup scant	55
Oysters	2 medium	15
Parsnip	1 large	55
Peach, canned, drained	2 halves	50
Peach, fresh	1 medium	40
Peanut butter	2 tablespoons	190
Peanuts	18 nuts, medium	110
Pears, canned, drained	2 halves	60
Pear, fresh	1 medium	50
Peas, canned	½ cup	95
Peas, fresh	½ cup	55
Pecans	12 halves	100
Pepper, green	1 large	25
Pickles	4″ x 1½″ x 1½″	15
Pineapple, canned, drained	1 slice	70
Pineapple, crushed	1 tablespoon	25

Pineapple, fresh	2 slices ¾" thick each	85
Pistachio nuts	10 large	35
Plums	3 medium	80
Popcorn, popped	1½ cup	100
Popover	1	100
Pork chop, lean	1 medium large	250
Pork chop, lean	1 medium small	190
Pork sausage, cooked	1⅔ sausages 3" long, ¾" diameter	100
Potato, white	2" x 4"	90
Potato, sweet	2" x 4"	180
Potato chips	8-10 large	100
Prune pulp	1 tablespoon	20
Prunes	1 very large	50
Prunes	1 medium	25
Puddings, commercial (made with skimmed milk)		
Butterscotch	½ cup	140
Chocolate	½ cup	150
Chocolate tapioca	½ cup	140
Orange tapioca	½ cup	140
Vanilla	½ cup	130
Vanilla tapioca	½ cup	130
Pumpkin	½ cup	20
Radishes	5 medium	10
Raisins, seeded	¼ cup	100
Raisins, seedless	2 tablespoons	100
Raspberries	½ cup	45
Rhubarb, fresh	1 cup, 1" pieces	20
Rice, dry	2 tablespoons	80
Rice, puffed	1 cup	75
Rice, steamed	½ cup	80
Rice pudding	⅓ cup	100
Rolls, French, hard	1	100
Romaine	10 leaves	15

Caloric Index

Salmon, canned	½ cup	100
Salmon, fresh, raw	2½ ounces	145
Salmon, smoked	3½ ounces	200
Sardines, drained	2 large or 4 small	80
Sauerkraut	½ cup	25
Scallops	½ cup	75
Shad, raw	3½ ounces	160
Shad roe	3⅓ ounces	130
Shredded wheat	1	105
Shrimps, cooked and peeled	⅔ cup	100
Smelts	2	30
Soups, canned		
Green turtle	½ cup	70
Mock turtle	½ cup	50
Mulligatawny	½ cup	45
Oxtail	½ cup	55
Split pea	½ cup	100
Tomato	½ cup	50
Vegetable	½ cup	20
Spaghetti, cooked	¾ cup	100
Spaghetti, cooked, diet	¾ cup	40
Spareribs	6 ribs	250
Spinach, cooked	½ cup	25
Squab	1 small	140
Squash, Hubbard, cooked	½ cup	45
Squash, summer, cooked	½ cup	15
Strawberries	½ cup	30
Sugar, brown	1 tablespoon	35
Sugar, white	1 cup	840
Sugar, white	2 tablespoons	105
Sweetbreads, cooked	¾ cup	175
Tapioca	1 tablespoon	50
Tangerine	1 medium	35
Tapioca pudding	⅖ cup	100
Tomato	1 medium	20

Tomato, cooked	½ cup scant	20
Tomato juice	⅓ cup	15
Tomato sauce	⅓ cup	100
Tongue	1 ounce	55
Triscuit	6	100
Trout, brook, raw	3½ ounces	95
Trout, lake, raw	3½ ounces	165
Tuna fish, canned, drained	½ cup	100
Turkey	4″ x 2¼″ x ¼″	100
Turnip, cooked	½ cup	35
Vinegar	1 tablespoon	0
Veal chop, lean	1 medium	125
Veal roast, lean	4½″ x 2¾″ x ⅛″	50
Veal kidney	7 ounces	250
Veal liver (calves)	3½″ x 2½″ x ½″	100
Waffle	6″ diameter	250
Walnuts	10 halves	100
Watercress	9 pieces	5
Watermelon	¾″ slice, 6″ diameter	100
Welsh rarebit	¼ cup sauce, 1 piece toast	210
Wheatena	2 tablespoons	75
Whitefish	3½ ounces	150
Whitefish, smoked	3″ x 2½″ x 1″	145
Yeast	2 cakes	35
Zwieback	3¼″ x 1¼″ x ½″	35
Zwieback, diet rusks	2	15

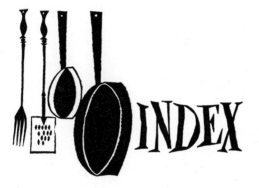

General Index

Recipe Index

Cereal and Egg Dishes
Cheese Soufflé, 42
Cornflakes with Sliced Strawberries, 97
Curried Chopped Egg Salad, 76
Eggs au Beurre Noir, 73
French Toast, 91
Herb Omelet, 67
Poached Egg, 88
Soufflé Omelet Parmesan, 79
Western Omelet, 55

Fish
Baked Oysters, 100
Cold Lobster with Celery Root Salad, 41
Coquilles St. Jacques, 76
Curried Shrimp, 59
Deviled Crabmeat, 49
Filet of Sole Soufflé, 52
Fish Rolls with Lemon Sauce, 93
Fresh Salmon and Cucumber Salad, 30
Lobster Farci, 67
Shad Roe, 89
Shrimp Salad, 82
Tomato Stuffed with Crabmeat, 61

Meat
Baked Ham with Mustard Sauce, 74
Baked Steak with Mushrooms, 85
Boiled Beef with Horseradish Sauce, 31
Calves Liver and Veal Kidney Flambé, 103
Chicken Fricassee, 82
Chicken in Wine, Fines Herbes, 71
Chicken Livers and Mushrooms Sauté, 79
Corned Beef, 48
Crisp Bacon, 42
De Luxe Chicken Chow Mein, 108

143

Grilled Frankfurters with Piquant Mustard, 114
Grilled Hamburgers with Barbecue Sauce, 111
Hamburger, 27
Hungarian Chicken Paprika, 36
Hungarian Pork Goulash, 91
Lamb Chops, 107
Pot Roast in Red Wine, 61
Roast Leg of Lamb, 34
Roast Veal, 55
Shish Kebab, 44
Spaghetti with Italian Meat Sauce, 64
Swedish Stuffed Cabbage, 39
Sweetbreads Supreme, 97
Veal Meatballs in Dill Sauce, 100
Veal Scallopini in Wine, 28

Vegetables

Artichoke, 80
Artichoke with Drawn Butter, 101
Asparagus Tips Polonaise, 50
Asparagus Vinaigrette, 68
Baked Acorn Squash, 74
Baked Tomato Stuffed with Cucumber, 86
Braised Celery, 98
Broccoli, 37
Brussels Sprouts, 112
Carrot Sticks, 42
Cauliflower, 28
Corn on the Cob, 71
Creamed Spinach, 74
Cucumber Wedges, 106
Fresh Asparagus Tips, 77
Fresh Peas, 107
Glacéed Carrots, 34

Hungarian Sauerkraut, 56
Lima Beans, 77
Minted Fresh Peas, 53
Peas à la Française, 34
Peas and Carrots, 83
Pickled Beets, 27
Sautéed Mushrooms on Toast, 33
Savoy Cabbage, 48
Spinach Soufflé, 94
String Beans Almondine, 71
Succotash, 98
Summer Squash, 95
Sweet and Sour String Beans, 89
Tomato Provençal, 45
Vegetable Plate with Poached Egg, Anchovy Sauce, 88

Potatoes, Noodles, etc.

Baked Stuffed Potato, 68
Boiled Rice, 80
Bouillon Potato, 31
Broad Noodles with Parmesan Cheese, 28
Caraway Potatoes, 92
Diet Spaghetti, 101
German Potato Salad, 115
Hungarian Egg Dumplings, 37
New Potatoes with Dill, 40
Pan Fried Noodles, 109
Parsleyed Rice, 104
Parsley Potato, 90
Potato Parmesan, 112
Saffron Rice, 59
Scalloped Potatoes, 86
Spaghetti with Italian Meat Sauce, 64
Whipped Potatoes, 56

Recipe Index

Set in Linotype Electra
Format by Marguerite Swanton
Manufactured by The Haddon Craftsmen, Inc.
Published by HARPER & BROTHERS, *New York*